DEAR READER:

We at **FANAFTER** know you had many options to choose from, we thank you for choosing us.

If you don't mind taking two minutes to share your experience with other shoppers, it'll be a great help 😊.

FUNAFTER
BOOKS

ISBN: 9798719347394

Contents

Word search rules:

Locate the given words in the grid, running in one of eight possible directions horizontally, vertically, or diagonally.

Example:

Puzzle

Solution

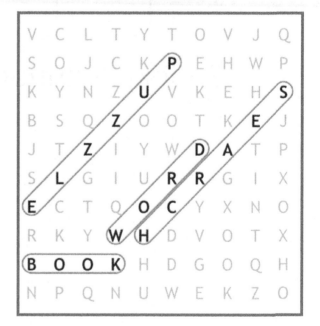

book puzzle search word

Sudoku rules:

Each of the nine blocks has to contain all the numbers 1-9 within its squares. Each number can only appear once in a row, column or box.

Example:

Puzzle

2	4		8			6		9
	6		3		9			2
		9				4		
5				3			9	
						3	7	
			4				6	
	9	6		8	4			5
	2		1		6		3	7
	8				9			

Solution

2	4	3	8	7	5	6	1	9
8	6	1	3	4	9	7	5	2
7	5	9	2	6	1	4	8	3
5	7	4	6	3	8	2	9	1
6	1	8	9	5	2	3	7	4
9	3	2	4	1	7	5	6	8
3	9	6	7	8	4	1	2	5
4	2	5	1	9	6	8	3	7
1	8	7	5	2	3	9	4	6

WORD SEARCH

Assorted Words 1

```
S  G  N  I  S  U  F  C  I  D  A  R  O  P  S
S  R  D  H  P  A  R  G  O  T  U  A  U  R  E
B  M  E  M  A  L  F  N  I  P  Z  E  I  U  E
P  P  U  K  R  E  C  A  N  T  M  D  Q  D  H
I  R  C  I  C  O  N  V  I  C  T  E  D  E  P
N  E  I  O  R  A  S  E  O  T  Q  M  Z  N  E
P  H  N  S  M  A  H  E  L  M  U  F  O  T  R
R  I  G  C  R  S  L  W  C  K  D  N  C  L  F
I  S  Q  O  R  E  E  O  H  I  C  R  I  Y  E
C  T  B  P  T  O  L  C  S  S  F  U  S  M  C
K  O  P  I  G  L  O  L  R  T  U  I  R  Z  T
I  R  M  Q  I  Z  R  K  E  O  U  B  R  T  E
N  I  X  D  R  A  W  R  E  T  F  A  F  O  S
G  C  T  C  A  R  T  E  R  D  N  N  W  Z  T
G  S  E  I  T  N  U  A  J  V  Z  W  E  D  I
```

AFTERWARD	INFLAME	RECANT
AUTOGRAPH	JAUNTIES	RETRACT
BUSHWHACKERS	MINUTIA	SOLARIUMS
CONVICTED	ORIFICES	SPORADIC
CROOKED	PERFECTEST	TELLERS
DEUCING	PINPRICKING	TRUCKLE
ENFORCES	PREHISTORIC	
FUSING	PRUDENTLY	

Assorted Words 2

```
G  J  Q  E  Y  T  S  A  H  G  S  U  H  X  H
R  C  P  W  E  S  L  Z  C  N  A  J  O  A  N
O  I  S  A  U  S  E  D  I  R  O  Y  I  G  U
U  M  G  E  D  S  E  V  B  O  N  K  I  U
C  E  C  N  A  R  D  N  I  H  O  B  N  T  V
H  S  S  E  I  P  E  E  I  V  S  O  A  A  F
E  S  I  N  Z  R  O  D  Y  L  O  D  Z  T  C
S  V  P  T  R  I  A  R  E  E  A  R  H  E  Q
H  L  O  R  I  E  L  E  T  E  K  C  P  D  S
Q  G  T  K  C  H  T  A  P  P  M  N  S  M  E
M  N  A  C  N  X  C  N  R  P  U  E  O  E  I
X  X  S  E  L  O  S  N  I  T  A  R  R  M  M
J  H  H  N  D  D  B  J  O  D  N  S  P  S  Z
S  S  U  O  I  R  E  S  Y  R  X  E  I  L  G
K  I  C  K  O  F  F  T  W  X  B  S  C  D  E
```

ACROBAT	HASTY	MONKEYED
AGITATED	HINDRANCE	PADRE
BOOZES	IMPROVISES	POTASH
BRONCHITIS	INSOLES	PURPLE
CANNON	INTERNS	REDEEMERS
CENTRALIZE	KICKOFF	SEAPORT
DISAPPEARING	KNOBS	SERIOUS
GROUCHES	MESCALINE	

Puzzle #3

Assorted Words 3

```
U K J J S P I H C O R C I M Z
S L I G H T B H D E K O O R E
Q E S C H U M O N G O U S B C
W X I G O C M T N E I C N A Q
H I J C N L O B U F F I N G U
Y E N T N I E M G N I K I L I
C C R F E E N S E N S R D S N
A T N I L L B R L L Q J E F T
V E S E T U N M O A Y O Y S E
Y Q Y C D A E I U C W S E O S
W I S Y A N G N I C X Y L B S
J Y L I R E E E Z L N L I B E
E C N A M O R P Q A R I D I N
O I D I S I N H E R I T S N C
H M O L L I F I E D L M I G E
```

ANCIENT	EERILY	MICROCHIPS
BONFIRES	EYELID	MOLLIFIED
BUFFING	HERITAGE	QUINTESSENCE
COLESLAW	HUMONGOUS	ROMANCE
COMELY	INCUMBENCIES	ROOKED
CORNING	INFLUENZA	SLIGHT
DEPENDENCY	INLET	SOBBING
DISINHERITS	LIKING	

Assorted Words 4

```
N V Z N C S L A I R O T C I P
M E A Y H A R E F I N E R Y O
S R G F T E S R E T C E P S S
L E X A I T R E L B B I R D I
W C K G N C A E W I G H R M T
E T A O O G I C A O Z A O A I
I P D D V S L O X F R S U T N
N R X E E N S I N Z T K T T G
C A E L R M O I O A C E E E J
U N V I U E A C P N D N R R U
B K G G M Q B N W P S O C I S
A S X H G Y J M K W I P S N Y
T T W T J Q T L U C T N M G N
E E E L J T K S E L I D G U U
D R X Y G N I N O I T N E M P
```

AFICIONADOS	HEREAFTER	POSITING
CASEWORKERS	INCUBATED	PRANKSTER
CATTY	LIGHTLY	PUMPS
CONVOKES	LUMBERED	REFINERY
DRIBBLER	MATTERING	ROUTE
ERECT	MENTIONING	SPECTERS
GANGLION	NICKNAMED	STYMIE
GOSSIPPING	PICTORIALS	

Assorted Words 5

```
P  I  C  C  S  R  E  T  I  R  W  Y  P  O  C
A  S  D  O  X  P  N  N  C  W  J  D  C  H  Z
T  Q  E  N  O  D  E  T  A  I  N  E  D  W  L
H  R  L  G  F  G  P  W  P  I  E  P  T  C  R
E  E  I  R  O  O  X  I  T  Z  M  R  U  D  J
T  S  B  E  Q  L  S  B  I  R  V  E  E  B  Q
I  T  E  G  N  K  D  S  V  W  N  A  H  R  R
C  F  R  A  G  O  M  E  I  N  K  M  Z  O  E
X  U  A  T  L  N  B  F  T  L  W  B  M  C  B
B  L  T  E  L  Y  O  K  I  L  S  L  A  H  E
N  M  I  D  I  O  O  I  E  U  A  E  I  U  L
P  D  O  L  D  R  U  M  S  E  Z  X  Z  R  L
L  X  N  L  I  V  N  T  Y  N  H  V  E  E  E
C  R  I  P  P  L  E  D  J  D  E  C  S  O  D
Q  S  H  F  T  A  R  C  I  N  G  T  E  Y  N
```

APLOMB	CRIPPLED	PREAMBLE
ARCING	DELIBERATION	REBELLED
BOHEMIAN	DETAINED	RESTFUL
BROCHURE	DOLDRUMS	TENSION
CAPTIVITIES	EXALTED	
CHEEKBONE	FOSSILS	
CONGREGATED	MAIZES	
COPYWRITERS	PATHETIC	

Assorted Words 6

```
C  A  J  P  E  N  I  S  G  S  I  W  D  F  E
G  P  U  R  I  T  A  N  F  U  R  J  Z  O  I
Q  N  S  E  L  D  D  U  P  F  P  E  K  R  J
Q  D  I  V  E  R  G  I  N  G  O  F  N  N  V
F  X  A  T  B  D  M  Z  H  C  P  L  B  I  Z
B  A  T  T  A  L  I  O  N  G  E  A  L  C  L
G  C  D  D  F  I  O  Q  S  D  C  T  H  A  I
N  O  I  T  A  L  L  O  C  Y  K  T  Z  T  F
E  S  E  O  A  F  X  I  P  V  E  E  A  I  A
U  M  D  T  Z  N  B  K  C  E  D  S  N  O  N
N  D  B  N  A  E  J  A  B  N  R  T  R  N  N
S  O  U  A  A  R  D  E  T  R  O  S  N  O  C
E  B  B  P  S  L  E  X  T  R  I  C  A  T  E
N  H  W  D  G  S  S  P  A  S  S  A  B  L  Y
T  B  K  Q  U  A  Y  I  O  W  I  N  G  E  R
```

BATTALION	FALLOFFS	PENIS
BLOOPER	FLATTEST	PUDDLES
COLLATION	FORNICATION	PURITAN
CONCILIATING	ISLANDS	UNSENT
CONSORTED	LINERS	WINGER
DIVERGING	OPERATE	
EMBASSY	PASSABLY	
EXTRICATE	PECKED	

Puzzle #7

Assorted Words 7

```
M R R B K W E D H E M A J M I
F Q E E O G S L E N I T C A M
Y R S I I S N T D T I G Q R P
K L A E T D L I N R F Y U Q E
R C S N C T O A D A U I G U T
M D O U K N I O O N R H G I U
X O E G O I E R M C E O D S O
G U A T N I N G G E R B N A U
L F C K S I C C R S G A M G S
A O P U G U T S E E D A H U I
D Q G T C V D H U N V L R C P
D S N I F F I R G L S I S A F
E F A M I L I A R I Z E D P G
S M A L S L O B B E R H P Q W
T P R O B O S C I S E F X D U
```

BENDING
CHARCOALS
DIVERGENCES
DUSTED
ENTRANCES
FAMILIARIZED
FRANKINCENSE
FRIGHTING

GARAGE
GIFTED
GLADDEST
GRIFFINS
GRITTIER
HURDLE
IGNORANTS
IMPETUOUS

LUSCIOUSLY
MARQUIS
MOODIER
PROBOSCIS
SLAMS
SLOBBER

13

Assorted Words 8

```
A Z E E D E T S A B M A L W G
Y I S V B E F A M I S H E S E
O U G T A A L D E R W O M A N
I X S A E D B G I D S P P V E
O U C S S N E E N S V V W A R
C W R H X L G D L I K P H R I
C S E O C C I Y S S P I O M C
I C E W U L N G C E J M L I A
D H C I G O S A H A U W E N L
E U H N D V K G U T R G S T L
N S Y G H E O V E R S E A S Y
T S L S D R A Y N R A B X L B
A I D I S C L A I M I N G F P
L N H U C K L E B E R R I E S
U G D W O H G L A M O R O U S
```

ALDERWOMAN
BABELS
BARNYARDS
BEGINS
BIRDS
CLOVER
CYGNETS
DISCLAIMING

EVADED
FAMISHES
GASLIGHTS
GENERICALLY
GLAMOROUS
HUCKLEBERRIES
LAMBASTED
OCCIDENTAL

OVERSEAS
PLAGUES
SCHUSSING
SCREECHY
SHOWINGS
TEMPING
VARMINTS
WHOLE

Assorted Words 9

```
S  E  Z  I  C  I  T  I  L  O  P  E  D  G  D
C  V  K  X  Y  I  M  P  R  O  V  E  S  S  D
S  O  A  S  L  A  T  N  E  M  A  D  N  U  F
F  T  C  X  K  B  C  S  R  O  R  R  O  H  W
X  R  N  K  K  H  G  N  I  T  N  U  P  V  G
M  S  Z  I  S  D  E  C  A  N  T  E  R  O  E
I  U  L  E  O  U  S  N  F  Q  U  M  N  J  N
N  B  H  E  R  N  C  S  K  G  M  M  Z  S  E
E  C  E  B  R  E  A  K  A  B  L  E  M  C  R
R  U  E  C  M  U  K  D  E  P  H  R  J  O  I
A  L  H  S  H  Z  S  C  E  R  M  I  E  O  C
L  T  A  N  J  S  R  S  A  U  S  O  X  P  E
O  U  W  H  Q  Z  U  R  I  R  R  H  C  S  H
G  R  E  T  R  E  A  D  S  F  C  T  K  Z  J
Y  E  D  I  N  V  E  S  T  I  T  U  R  E  S
```

ANOINTS	FISSURE	PUNTING
BREAKABLE	FUNDAMENTALS	RETREADS
COCKSUCKERS	GENERIC	SCOOPS
COMMUNISTIC	HEEHAWED	SUBCULTURE
COMPASS	HORRORS	TRUED
CRACKER	IMPROVES	
DECANTER	INVESTITURES	
DEPOLITICIZES	MINERALOGY	

Assorted Words 10

```
E  T  I  R  W  R  E  V  O  S  Q  Y  S  C  Q
A  S  Y  A  W  T  R  A  P  Q  N  W  N  I  R
S  M  U  K  S  I  U  M  B  M  U  I  I  C  M
Y  E  B  O  D  S  D  B  O  T  H  H  F  A  S
P  L  T  I  M  E  E  B  B  L  D  H  F  T  T
L  M  S  A  T  E  N  N  B  X  D  M  L  R  Y
A  U  A  U  I  I  H  O  I  H  N  S  E  I  R
I  Y  R  R  O  D  O  P  E  S  S  T  S  X  A
T  C  I  H  T  E  E  U  S  G  S  I  N  E  N
S  U  R  E  W  N  D  M  S  A  N  O  L  S  T
D  E  T  A  R  E  B  I  L  L  L  U  L  W  S
Y  T  I  V  A  C  F  P  H  X  Y  B  D  G  O
P  U  S  S  I  E  R  M  E  A  T  B  A  L  L
X  Q  E  Q  Y  L  B  A  R  O  L  P  E  D  D
P  B  R  U  S  Q  U  E  N  E  S  S  H  D  Y
```

AMBITIOUSLY	GLOSSINESS	OWLISH
BLASPHEMOUS	HIDEOUSLY	PARTWAY
BOBBIES	LIBERATED	PLAITS
BRUSQUENESS	MEATBALL	PUSSIER
CAVITY	MEDIATES	SNIFFLES
CICATRIXES	MOLDS	TRAMP
DEPLORABLY	NIFTY	TYRANTS
DUNGEONED	OVERWRITE	

Assorted Words 11

```
E P R O P E L L E D Z U H V Q
V N K L R O R G A N I S M S B
N Y O N E S T L I N G P K L H
R T Q R D M E T A B O L I S M
P R E M I S E T J P B X L S S
S A S F C W R B O M N O S Y L
I I T B T Z D E P I A S N B A
X L A U S A E I R O L A Y S U
T I T D S S D T S A S S J Y G
I N E S W H S E I P E K O F H
E G S D E T A M K C E H C M T
T J M L Z C F V V N N N Z D E
H E A D H U N T E R A I S U R
S W N U Y K O E L D A L M E E
I H D C L R E I F O O G F Z D
```

CHECKMATED	INCITE	SIXTIETHS
DISPENSED	METABOLISM	SLAUGHTERED
FENCE	NESTLING	STATESMAN
FLANKED	ORGANISMS	TOILSOME
GIBBONS	PREDICTS	TRAILING
GOOFIER	PREMISE	
HEADHUNTER	PROPELLED	
HEARER	SHAVED	

Assorted Words 12

```
L  J  B  R  E  T  N  E  I  C  N  A  F  H  C
K  S  A  Y  O  P  I  N  S  T  R  I  P  E  S
I  I  W  G  L  O  C  O  W  E  E  D  G  A  V
P  M  F  L  O  S  F  O  D  S  I  E  B  B  P
Y  P  P  L  Q  I  S  A  L  E  R  L  T  S  P
R  L  S  L  I  P  E  E  D  Q  N  J  M  H  R
O  I  P  D  U  V  E  M  L  E  G  I  O  E  E
T  S  A  P  R  G  E  R  I  T  T  W  P  F  M
E  T  S  R  U  A  N  R  S  T  R  T  P  O  I
C  I  T  F  E  S  C  I  Y  U  T  A  I  X  E
H  C  S  G  D  P  R  T  N  I  A  H  N  M  R
N  L  K  R  T  A  O  E  S  R  H  S  G  I  E
I  V  A  N  J  S  A  S  V  O  A  M  I  I  D
C  F  L  V  B  U  C  Q  E  O  P  E  E  O  N
U  A  F  R  A  S  H  E  R  S  L  W  F  A  N
```

ANCIENTER	NIGHTTIME	PYROTECHNIC
ARTLESSLY	OPINED	RASHERS
EARNING	OVERSUPPLY	REPOSES
EMITTED	PASTS	SIMPLISTIC
ENCROACH	PERSUASION	TEETHE
LIVERY	PINSTRIPES	
LOCOWEED	POSTCARDS	
MOPPING	PREMIERED	

Assorted Words 13

```
Q  G  V  E  T  E  R  E  I  K  R  U  M  L  N
N  J  N  T  I  N  V  I  G  O  R  A  T  E  X
L  W  G  I  A  O  A  B  P  U  M  P  K  I  N
E  W  C  N  H  Z  E  R  A  C  R  E  A  G  E
A  C  O  M  I  C  S  G  G  L  Z  H  L  V  G
T  G  O  I  V  L  T  G  N  I  D  D  E  B  I
H  O  B  T  D  D  E  I  N  I  M  N  C  Q  L
E  R  I  D  D  E  D  H  W  R  P  M  E  N  P
R  C  O  L  O  R  F  A  S  T  E  P  I  S  C
Y  U  L  P  V  X  M  F  I  U  I  G  A  Z  S
K  I  D  D  Y  I  N  G  U  U  B  L  N  C  H
W  K  O  S  J  U  Q  H  E  R  N  I  A  A  V
D  E  L  O  D  L  T  P  M  W  G  A  N  D  M
X  S  P  D  E  N  O  U  N  C  I  N  G  W  A
E  G  N  I  T  C  A  T  N  O  C  E  K  F  G
```

ACREAGE	DENOUNCING	MANGER
BALDNESS	DOLED	MURKIER
BEDDING	GRUFFED	PUMPKIN
BUSHELING	HERNIA	RIDDED
CAPPING	IMMIGRANT	TWITCHING
COLORFAST	INVIGORATE	
COMICS	KIDDYING	
CONTACTING	LEATHERY	

Assorted Words 14

```
Y  S  I  Q  E  G  N  I  M  M  I  R  N  N  L
G  L  S  N  I  D  G  N  I  C  C  E  P  S  I
D  U  A  S  T  X  U  Z  O  R  E  V  I  L  S
S  N  R  T  A  E  J  T  E  S  I  Y  D  F  T
N  B  O  M  D  R  R  V  I  K  E  B  S  B  L
L  I  N  H  U  A  C  W  S  P  M  Q  J  M  E
G  U  O  W  L  T  O  L  E  T  E  O  U  B  S
S  N  C  G  L  O  N  G  H  A  I  R  M  E  S
X  E  I  A  R  I  J  E  L  U  V  W  C  M  L
T  C  V  T  N  L  U  C  M  L  E  I  T  E  Y
Y  N  B  L  I  C  R  T  T  R  A  V  N  I  D
N  R  E  N  A  N  E  E  L  T  A  F  Q  G  N
M  U  B  V  Q  V  U  R  V  J  C  B  E  X  B
E  S  T  H  E  T  I  C  N  E  G  E  E  B  R
A  C  F  C  B  Q  D  B  G  S  F  D  J  D  M
```

BEFALL	EVENT	SEQUEL
BIVALVES	FEVER	SLIVER
CANCER	INTERWEAVING	SPECCING
CONJURE	LISTLESSLY	UNITING
CRASS	LONGHAIR	
DEBARMENT	MOMMY	
DECREPITUDE	NITWITS	
ESTHETIC	RIMMING	

Assorted Words 15

```
D E L P M I S D T N E V E R P
P C U R T S E Y E D V C S U A
E B U A E B D Y S G K D F G L
R R F P M O D E L A R J A U I
G N I R O S R U C K N A M B C
L Z X F L I N E A L U N D T K
O I A A E R S U R R A Z E E I
N Y T I Q S F E M F E I H H N
G O I F Z P A E I T Z B M A G
H U V U S N M E D N O C M E S
O P E R J U R Y C O M S S U D
R F D E K C A B H C N U H H Z
N D I S T A S T E F U L L Y Y
S C H I M M U T A B L Y W A T
F I L C H I N G N I D O O W C
```

CALUMNIES
CEASEFIRE
CONDEMNS
CURSORING
CURTSEYED
DECLAIMED
DEGRADE
DISTASTEFULLY

FILCHING
FIXATIVE
HENNAS
HUNCHBACKED
IMMUTABLY
LICKINGS
LINEAL
LONGHORNS

MODEL
NUMBER
PERJURY
PREVENT
SIMPLED
WOODING

Assorted Words 16

```
D  N  U  O  P  X  E  G  B  Y  B  U  A  Y  Z
I  E  M  O  U  S  I  N  G  S  O  L  E  O  C
S  P  C  O  Y  T  N  A  R  A  U  G  X  P  A
O  G  O  D  H  L  B  H  J  Y  N  E  P  P  O
R  F  N  B  S  D  A  E  H  H  C  A  E  B  B
D  O  F  I  J  K  B  S  H  A  E  P  C  E  S
E  U  U  Z  L  B  Y  N  E  I  S  O  T  T  O
R  L  S  Q  Q  T  S  W  G  R  P  T  O  R  L
C  L  I  T  C  P  I  N  X  T  E  T  R  A  E
V  Y  O  K  S  S  T  H  T  I  E  E  A  Y  S
S  Q  N  L  D  I  T  F  C  G  D  R  T  A  C
A  G  S  N  O  G  E  H  N  H  E  I  I  L  E
J  H  Q  X  V  U  R  H  G  T  D  N  N  W  N
K  R  I  U  R  O  S  I  C  N  I  G  G  Q  T
S  P  A  C  I  D  N  A  H  N  Y  K  X  N  Y
```

AIRTIGHT	EXPECTORATING	MOUSING
BABYSITTERS	EXPOUND	OBSOLESCENT
BEACHHEADS	FOULLY	POTTERING
BETRAYAL	GUARANTY	SPEEDED
BOUNCES	HANDICAPS	
CHITLINGS	HEIST	
CONFUSIONS	INCISOR	
DISORDER	LASER	

Assorted Words 17

```
D  A  N  S  C  O  M  P  E  L  L  E  D  P  O
R  E  N  C  E  O  B  X  B  O  H  L  N  O  V
A  N  F  A  X  R  L  K  W  M  F  A  R  T  L
C  E  P  A  C  J  U  O  M  U  M  M  E  R  S
C  W  C  O  U  H  A  T  N  U  C  E  S  N  N
O  S  Q  O  M  L  R  B  R  I  P  N  T  L  O
O  P  B  L  N  P  T  O  S  U  Z  T  O  B  O
N  A  L  E  H  S  A  E  N  C  N  E  C  O  P
S  P  B  M  Z  C  E  D  D  I  O  D  K  N  I
T  E  D  E  K  O  V  N  O  C  S  N  E  G  E
A  R  Z  N  J  F  P  Q  T  U  D  M  D  O  S
T  E  Q  D  N  E  U  E  X  I  R  E  S  S  T
I  D  E  M  O  L  I  T  I  O  N  E  D  G  O
O  W  E  A  K  E  S  T  E  E  R  G  D  I  S
N  B  S  E  T  A  M  I  T  S  E  W  E  E  S
```

ABSCONDS	DEMOLITION	POMPADOURED
ANACHRONISMS	EMEND	RACCOONS
BONGOS	ESTIMATES	RESTOCKED
COLONIZE	GREETS	SIDED
COMPELLED	LAMENTED	SNOOPIEST
CONSENTING	MUMMERS	STATION
CONVOKED	NEWSPAPERED	WEAKEST
DEFAULTED	NURTURES	

Assorted Words 18

```
I  F  R  D  D  E  N  O  U  E  M  E  N  T  S
Q  M  C  R  I  C  X  J  V  H  S  I  D  O  M
S  B  P  A  J  G  R  P  A  P  N  H  I  T  O
W  E  Z  R  M  R  I  A  E  U  R  T  U  L  R
G  L  I  Y  I  P  R  T  W  C  N  O  F  H  D
G  L  A  L  C  S  U  E  A  F  T  T  U  J  A
F  B  K  T  L  A  O  S  I  L  I  I  E  D  I
L  O  C  M  N  I  U  N  I  T  I  S  N  D  N
I  Y  O  E  E  E  B  Q  M  N  H  Z  H  G  S
B  J  V  T  T  S  M  L  E  E  G  G  E  I  D
E  Z  B  L  B  I  R  A  L  D  N  K  I  D  K
L  P  W  S  T  A  N  E  D  I  A  T  P  M  L
L  O  P  Z  X  R  L  G  V  N  H  N  K  Y  L
E  Q  P  R  E  V  O  L  I  N  U  T  I  B  O
R  Y  J  A  I  L  E  R  S  L  I  F  P  Y  D
```

BELLBOY	HILLBILLIES	LOVER
CAMPUSING	IMPRISONMENT	MIGHTIER
CRAWFISH	INADEQUACY	MODISH
DENOUEMENTS	INVERSE	ORDAINS
DIGITALIZED	JAILERS	PROUD
EXPECTING	JAUNTED	
FOOTBALLS	LIBELLER	
FUNDAMENTAL	LIGNITE	

Assorted Words 19

```
N  N  W  A  E  L  B  G  H  S  F  F  O  C  S
S  A  U  W  E  T  M  I  N  T  I  E  S  T  P
I  I  I  R  Q  M  A  I  H  I  Z  A  P  O  T
P  E  N  C  R  C  A  R  E  E  R  I  N  G  M
I  L  S  F  I  E  X  S  B  G  G  E  X  B  E
C  G  Q  D  U  R  V  A  T  E  A  Y  G  Y  B
K  T  U  F  U  L  T  O  A  O  L  S  Z  N  R
E  R  E  S  D  F  L  A  S  H  I  E  S  T  A
R  A  L  Y  S  C  D  Y  P  C  J  D  C  P  K
E  V  C  J  D  E  Y  E  B  O  S  I  D  Z  U
L  E  H  H  Y  R  T  E  M  E  L  E  T  A  G
S  L  E  M  Q  I  N  I  T  R  A  M  L  H  I
O  I  S  F  L  A  G  E  L  L  A  T  I  O  N
W  N  D  E  I  D  I  O  T  I  C  A  L  L  Y
D  G  O  S  S  E  S  A  E  R  C  N  A  P  R
```

ANGERING	IDIOTICALLY	SCOFFS
ARMED	MARTINI	SINFULLY
CAREERING	MASTOID	SQUELCHES
CELEBRATE	MINTIEST	TELEMETRY
DISOBEYED	OVERRUN	TOPAZ
FLAGELLATION	PANCREASES	TRAVELING
FLASHIEST	PATRICIAN	
GUSSET	PICKERELS	

Assorted Words 20

```
J  D  E  Z  A  F  C  X  K  D  T  N  O  R  I
F  V  X  M  S  J  C  O  W  O  R  R  O  S  M
R  E  C  K  P  D  S  R  P  A  U  X  F  M  M
E  S  E  M  U  F  L  P  E  P  P  D  P  G  U
E  A  P  T  V  O  Q  T  I  W  E  Z  B  E  N
L  L  T  A  N  Q  M  J  B  T  M  R  N  X  I
A  I  I  T  D  E  L  L  A  C  T  A  C  P  Z
N  P  O  J  R  L  M  O  I  K  V  E  N  A  E
C  S  N  M  C  A  D  R  T  L  T  N  D  T  S
I  T  A  Z  J  H  C  S  E  D  I  M  O  R  B
N  I  L  M  R  Y  O  T  U  T  H  W  L  I  Z
G  C  L  Y  S  A  A  P  I  L  T  P  R  A  P
G  K  Y  C  A  M  E  Z  P  O  L  E  H  T  T
S  U  O  N  I  T  U  L  G  E  N  E  B  E  O
S  R  E  L  Z  Z  U  G  X  O  R  S  N  S  Y
```

ATTRACTIONS	EXPATRIATES	SORROW
BETTERMENT	FAZED	SPITTED
BROMIDES	FREELANCING	SULLEN
CATCALLED	FUMES	
CHOPPER	GLUTINOUS	
COPPER	GUZZLERS	
CREWMAN	IMMUNIZES	
EXCEPTIONALLY	LIPSTICK	

Assorted Words 21

```
T  G  Y  W  M  A  S  H  E  R  T  Z  U  K  A
C  G  N  L  S  S  O  N  D  H  C  O  O  M  I
U  A  N  I  G  K  E  V  A  E  A  P  X  Q  L
S  T  L  I  T  N  N  O  Z  I  P  W  W  I  L
M  R  C  C  Y  C  I  D  D  C  T  E  W  L  N
A  A  D  A  U  A  U  R  I  S  O  N  E  P  E
U  S  M  P  M  L  L  D  I  S  I  N  E  T  S
S  H  C  E  M  E  A  E  N  U  P  M  G  G  S
O  E  Z  I  N  V  R  T  D  O  Q  L  M  A  E
L  S  L  U  Y  I  S  A  I  R  C  N  A  J  S
E  Z  A  T  N  N  L  I  S  O  O  S  I  C  R
A  G  F  B  T  C  H  E  G  D  N  L  I  P  E
F  I  N  I  T  E  L  Y  F  O  R  S  L  M  R
Z  G  H  N  E  S  K  A  I  E  Y  C  T  Y  P
A  A  O  Z  F  L  O  P  H  O  U  S  E  S  P
```

CALCULATIONS	FINITELY	MISCONDUCTING
CAMERAS	FLOPHOUSES	MISDOES
CONGAS	GENTIANS	MOOCH
DELAYING	ILLNESSES	STEEPED
DISPLACE	INQUIRINGLY	TRASHES
DROLLY	KETTLES	YOGIS
EVINCES	MASHER	
FELINE	MAUSOLEA	

Assorted Words 22

```
M R H C O M P O S I T I O N S
K L E G W S E I R A T O R H C
R I D D N S F R U I T F U L O
B N P J N I U L E G G I E R M
T O R T X E Z O B K M P C F M
Y L I R A R T I B R A X N X A
D E N K X B Z N L A Z E X P N
I U T N U L O Y O A N F R S D
S M O Y A G N R C C T N A B E
C B R E A K N E C K N U A Z E
I O J C O M B A T A N T R W R
P L D E T A C E R P E D W B S
L P R O P R I E T O R S M T R
E C Z J S E N I W T R E T N I
S C I T S A I S E L C C E F W
```

ACROBAT
ARBITRARILY
BREAKER
BREAKNECK
BRUTALIZING
COMBATANT
COMMANDEERS
COMPOSITIONS

CONTENDER
DEPRECATED
DISCIPLES
ECCLESIASTICS
FRUITFUL
INTERTWINES
LEGGIER
LINOLEUM

PRINT
PROPRIETORS
ROTARIES
WANNA

Assorted Words 23

```
L  S  Z  B  D  T  B  D  E  E  C  O  R  P  W
S  M  Q  U  C  H  U  K  V  V  S  O  E  R  A
E  A  B  G  L  I  O  W  I  V  S  U  M  O  L
R  R  A  G  N  X  B  N  L  I  Y  E  A  H  K
V  T  A  I  N  I  N  O  E  T  H  U  R  I  I
I  E  W  N  L  P  R  O  R  S  X  W  K  B  N
C  S  Q  G  S  H  O  E  S  E  T  O  I  I  G
I  T  T  X  J  N  A  S  T  D  A  Y  N  T  S
N  R  E  D  I  W  E  D  H  L  N  N  G  I  M
G  R  S  N  O  I  S  S  A  P  A  A  A  O  E
R  N  G  N  I  U  E  U  Q  C  E  V  R  N  L
E  V  O  K  E  R  G  O  N  O  M  I  C  G  T
V  M  I  Z  G  E  X  T  R  U  D  I  N  G  E
J  U  R  E  S  T  I  N  G  U  Q  X  U  M  R
W  O  G  I  K  P  A  C  D  E  R  E  N  J  S
```

ALTERING	EXTRUDING	REMARKING
ANAEROBIC	GRANDSON	RESTING
BUGGING	HONESTY	SERVICING
DAHLIA	PASSIONS	SMARTEST
ENSNARE	PROCEED	SMELTERS
ERGONOMIC	PROHIBITION	WALKING
EVILER	QUEUING	WIDER
EVOKE	REDCAP	

Assorted Words 24

```
H  P  Z  F  H  F  S  C  K  D  Q  N  J  L  P
I  C  G  O  S  A  A  R  T  A  V  F  C  S  E
S  P  H  D  E  S  R  R  O  M  E  B  C  Z  R
T  A  O  I  R  I  E  K  R  S  L  L  I  V  C
O  L  A  L  H  K  G  N  E  O  I  C  A  P  O
R  N  A  U  A  S  C  H  I  N  W  V  E  Z  L
I  E  A  T  M  R  U  O  T  S  I  S  H  V  A
A  S  S  E  N  D  L  O  C  E  S  H  B  I  T
N  A  R  S  C  E  P  S  N  Y  E  E  F  E  I
S  U  A  X  Z  A  M  N  N  E  P  N  R  O  N
Z  N  X  D  D  Y  T  I  O  I  G  P  S  D  G
S  U  B  T  I  T  L  E  R  N  P  I  O  F  V
G  N  I  P  P  A  W  S  C  T  E  P  D  P  E
K  X  D  U  P  L  I  C  A  T  E  S  I  N  S
H  O  M  O  G  E  N  E  O  U  S  D  D  P  I
```

AZALEA	EIGHTEENS	PIPPINS
CETACEAN	FARROWS	POLAR
COLDNESS	HARKEN	POPPYCOCK
DAMSONS	HISTORIANS	SUBTITLE
DETRIMENTAL	HOMOGENEOUS	SWAPPING
DILUTES	INDIGENOUS	VISORS
DRESSINESS	NONES	
DUPLICATES	PERCOLATING	

Assorted Words 25

```
O  L  S  E  N  A  T  I  V  I  T  I  E  S  O
U  H  O  D  L  S  B  D  S  I  F  H  S  B  N
T  C  L  V  N  O  I  R  E  N  Z  P  R  H  V
D  R  U  R  I  C  P  T  I  I  G  I  E  Q  L
I  E  B  D  E  N  S  E  I  Q  R  I  M  R  L
S  F  I  D  I  N  G  E  M  T  U  A  L  M  Y
T  E  L  R  A  F  I  L  N  E  A  E  L  A  D
A  R  I  A  E  S  F  L  Y  O  N  P  T  A  M
N  E  T  C  Y  G  H  U  R  C  B  T  E  S  S
C  N  Y  H  K  K  N  I  S  I  U  Y  S  H  E
E  D  G  M  K  T  S  I  N  I  A  G  Z  B  A
K  U  M  A  C  H  O  I  L  G  N  I  W  A  C
K  M  W  S  E  S  I  A  R  J  N  G  W  E  L
S  L  A  N  I  C  I  D  E  M  U  W  F  P  T
T  R  O  U  S  P  R  O  U  D  L  Y  Q  G  J
```

AIRLINER	HEPATITIS	OUTDISTANCE
ANNUL	LAZYBONES	PROUDLY
BRIQUETS	LINGERIE	RAISES
CAWING	LOVINGLY	REFERENDUM
DASHING	MACHO	RISKY
DIFFUSING	MALIGNS	SALARIED
DRACHMAS	MEDICINALS	SOLUBILITY
ELOPEMENTS	NATIVITIES	

Assorted Words 26

```
Z I N T E R C H A N G I N G I
X D R O W N S N O L Y N M O P
Y S O E B A N K R O L L S D H
K C E R T L L S L A P P E D I
H P A S K A E I P A Z D W P L
O A W P S I D A G N W J A E A
V U U U O A E E C N M B X Y N
E O K L F C P S S O M R W B T
R U X Z E S S M T U E E I U H
C O S X T D W I O N J E N S R
O R E I K C U L P C I Z G T O
M D M D D I N G I E R I S L P
I Y A S B E S T O S G N C E Y
N I B T H K H E F F I G Y S T
G V S T S I N O I T R O T X E
```

ALIGNMENT	DORKIEST	NYLONS
ANNOUNCES	DROWNS	OVERCOMING
ASBESTOS	EFFIGY	PHILANTHROPY
BANKROLLS	EPISCOPACY	PLUCKIER
BREEZING	EXTORTIONISTS	SEDATER
BUSTLES	HAULED	SLAPPED
COMPASSES	INTERCHANGING	WAXWINGS
DINGIER	NOBLE	

Assorted Words 27

```
S  O  J  U  D  G  I  N  G  U  P  R  G  E  M
N  R  U  Y  T  D  C  W  R  E  A  K  E  D  E
Q  F  E  C  O  S  E  O  D  A  Y  J  F  N
R  Z  A  T  S  R  R  R  N  K  X  A  S  E  S
I  O  C  N  S  S  L  E  E  S  Z  I  V  S  W
M  Y  T  O  R  K  E  I  G  F  E  A  T  T  E
B  R  C  U  N  D  C  N  M  N  F  N  K  I  A
E  E  O  R  B  F  R  U  H  B  I  I  T  V  R
C  C  G  V  A  I  I  A  H  S  O  T  D  E  A
I  E  A  U  N  P  R  D  U  Q  I  S  S  L  D
L  P  H  T  T  S  P  T  E  G  O  L  G  Y  D
I  T  P  A  E  W  R  I  N  N  D  I  U  R  E
T  O  X  X  R  R  F  Z  E  O  T  U  V  M  F
Y  R  I  P  S  V  E  B  R  S  C  L  M  U  S
P  G  R  A  P  E  F  R  U  I  T  S  Y  D  P
```

BANTERS	GRAPEFRUITS	RECEPTOR
CATERER	HUCKSTERS	STINGERS
CONFIDENTLY	IMBECILITY	WREAKED
CONSENTED	JUDGING	
CONTRIBUTOR	LIMBOS	
CRAPPIEST	MENSWEAR	
DIFFERED	MUDGUARD	
FESTIVELY	MULISHNESS	

Assorted Words 28

```
N E S R O L I C N U O C Z Q T
A N E U E H I S T R I O N I C
R G H U S T S I M R O F N O C
C T X S Q P A L M E D A X B I
I O K C D S Z R O B J L S L Z
S C R D S R A I E A X K W E O
S I H O E N E M T S M B O Y U
U O Q I L L O N C H I I R P K
S J U T S L B I N F A M E W Q
E Y T N I E A B S U L L M S I
S C N Q D R L R I L R N T O T
W K N U C K L E I N U E G U C
R E P U T I N G R E S P R T J
C O N N E C T O R S S N X O W
E I N V I D I O U S S J E E F
```

BASHFULNESS
CHISELERS
COMMISERATE
CONFORMISTS
CONNECTORS
COROLLARIES
COUNCILORS
EXPULSIONS

FORERUNNER
HISTRIONIC
INVIDIOUS
KNUCKLE
LOAMIEST
MASQUE
NARCISSUSES
NIBBLED

PALMED
REPUTING
SOUND
SWORE

Assorted Words 29

```
S R E K N A T S M R E T D I M
D E G S U B S I D I N G I Z C
T I G I U D E T C I V E Z Q O
O M S A H B A C K L O G S Z N
L L A D W G A V S A X R K M T
E O H R A E N G H P Z P D E U
R V T X R I N I N O J Z E N M
A E R R G I N A Y I O L E A A
B M Q E I N A F C F D P R C C
L A V R I C I G U T I A S E I
E K F L Q S K L E L M R F H O
L I K E N E S S Z A L E O E U
D N O P S E R O T Z B Y N L S
O G E B B Q K U L E U L N T G
G N I N O S A E R G R N E K I
```

ANDROIDS	GLORIFYING	NUZZLING
BACKLOGS	GLOSSIER	REASONING
CONTUMACIOUS	HOOPS	RESPOND
DEERS	LIKENESS	SUBSIDING
DISDAINFULLY	LOVEMAKING	TANKERS
ENACTMENT	MARRIAGEABLE	TOLERABLE
EVICTED	MENACE	TRICKSTER
FADING	MIDTERMS	WAGES

Assorted Words 30

```
D C S O D S T S I C I R Y L M
E I E C D E E P E R S O N S E
A T S D O N R G G L L F R P R
L N A I E M C U Y V A E E H R
R O T M N C P E T E C C F X Y
P V W I P F C A U L D R O N M
J C M N S L E A T Q U T R L A
I I I U E E E C W I J C M E K
T R R H C S P H T P B D S X E
O Q X O D U S T E D W L T P R
D U P L I C A T I O N G Y L Z
S R E K A E R B E C I V X A I
C H U R C H G O E R S K S I P
S U O I G I L E R R I W S N U
Q Y L L A T N E D I C C A S L
```

ACCEDE
ACCIDENTALLY
ANTISEPTICS
CAULDRON
CHURCHGOERS
COMPATIBLY
CULTURED
DISINFECT

DUPLICATION
DUSTED
EXPLAINS
HELPMATE
ICEBREAKERS
IRRELIGIOUS
LOCALES
LOWNESS

LYRICISTS
MERRYMAKER
PERSONS
REFORMS

Assorted Words 31

```
B  N  V  J  N  O  N  D  R  I  N  K  E  R  Y
S  Y  M  D  D  G  L  U  N  C  H  R  O  O  M
T  L  L  O  U  Y  R  O  T  A  B  U  C  N  I
O  K  U  N  O  I  T  A  U  T  E  P  R  E  P
D  A  Z  F  X  N  O  I  T  A  T  S  T  U  O
G  B  A  O  D  E  Z  I  T  I  R  O  I  R  P
I  W  L  S  T  E  H  S  E  R  F  R  Q  U  B
E  A  E  A  O  B  E  G  N  I  F  E  E  R  J
S  D  R  O  C  C  A  N  W  O  H  S  M  N  O
T  I  T  L  L  K  R  E  I  D  N  A  S  J  G
N  E  N  Y  R  U  B  I  E  D  X  G  R  G  G
N  S  E  M  P  C  P  A  R  T  E  R  I  F  L
N  Q  S  Y  T  I  C  I  L  E  F  N  I  Z  I
M  Q  S  D  U  Z  R  E  D  L  O  S  O  W  N
T  W  E  Z  I  L  I  B  A  T  S  E  D  V  G
```

ACCORDS	JOGGLING	RUBIED
ALERTNESS	LUNCHROOM	SANDIER
BLACKBALLS	NEEDFULS	SHOWN
DESTABILIZE	NONDRINKER	SOLDER
FIRETRAP	OUTSTATION	STODGIEST
FRESHETS	PERPETUATION	WADIES
INCUBATOR	PRIORITIZED	
INFELICITY	REEFING	

Assorted Words 32

```
R  V  G  N  I  D  R  A  L  R  E  T  N  I  D
E  N  M  P  I  S  K  C  O  T  S  R  E  V  O
S  R  C  E  G  N  I  R  P  S  D  N  A  H  D
P  H  T  A  R  K  S  U  M  J  K  B  V  V  E
E  H  V  Q  J  I  J  B  G  U  Q  O  X  A  M
L  A  I  N  N  E  T  N  E  C  I  B  V  N  U
L  H  W  Y  G  N  I  G  G  A  L  F  X  A  R
S  D  K  O  K  S  O  W  S  T  R  F  D  L  R
Y  J  C  E  C  A  L  I  P  E  R  S  E  Y  E
O  U  E  S  W  K  E  E  P  S  I  E  K  S  D
R  U  F  F  L  E  S  L  U  Y  W  T  S  I  K
X  S  N  O  T  O  H  P  J  F  N  E  S  S  N
K  G  E  R  M  I  N  A  T  I  O  N  L  A  A
O  P  S  E  D  I  C  I  M  R  E  G  U  S  P
E  J  P  E  R  C  A  L  E  S  F  N  X  R  I
```

ANALYSIS	GERMICIDES	PASTIES
ASSERT	GERMINATION	PERCALES
BEARSKIN	HANDSPRING	PHOTONS
BICENTENNIAL	INTERLARDING	RESPELLS
CALIPER	LEAKY	RUFFLES
DEMURRED	MERIT	RUNNY
FLAGGING	MUSKRAT	SLEWS
FUELS	OVERSTOCKS	

Assorted Words 33

```
W  Z  V  G  Y  L  L  A  N  O  I  T  A  N  W
B  W  O  J  N  F  R  E  T  I  C  E  N  C  E
D  U  O  Y  S  I  E  P  B  H  G  F  R  I  M
S  A  I  U  Q  O  L  L  O  C  I  H  D  X  S
R  E  K  C  I  H  T  T  I  T  T  A  T  H  P
Y  E  S  N  U  C  K  N  S  C  E  J  M  L  F
D  T  W  O  A  L  L  V  A  U  I  E  W  I  Y
L  E  N  S  P  C  L  L  W  C  H  T  R  M  N
S  E  T  E  J  X  B  I  R  D  E  D  I  T  A
E  L  S  A  I  N  E  D  T  J  H  D  U  E  P
T  C  F  A  G  T  D  R  E  S  S  I  N  G  S
T  Y  I  G  E  O  A  B  E  F  I  T  Q  J  U
E  C  U  X  I  N  R  P  A  V  N  D  R  S  Z
E  O  Y  E  C  N  U  E  M  Y  O  A  L  A  E
S  N  A  T  C  H  E  S  D  I  Y  D  G  C  P
```

BIRDED	IMPATIENT	SNUCK
CANTOS	NATIONALLY	THIAMIN
COLLOQUIA	NIGHTLY	THICKER
DEROGATED	OVEREXPOSES	TREETOP
DISTILL	PARTS	UNEASE
DRESSING	RETICENCE	
FELICITIES	SETTEES	
HUSTLING	SNATCHES	

Assorted Words 34

```
O  S  N  O  I  T  A  C  I  F  I  D  O  M  V
K  T  A  F  M  I  D  W  I  F  E  S  X  G  W
T  E  S  D  E  Z  I  R  U  T  A  I  N  I  M
E  R  S  L  S  J  T  F  U  N  K  Y  J  R  H
T  R  U  E  A  R  K  S  Y  R  E  A  F  X  G
A  O  R  W  D  T  E  N  E  E  Y  V  O  J  P
R  R  E  T  I  O  I  T  C  I  V  T  F  P  L
N  S  D  O  S  S  B  P  H  O  T  R  A  E  U
I  R  L  I  C  K  E  A  A  G  U  S  U  S  M
S  P  Y  L  O  Y  S  A  P  C  I  P  U  S  B
H  O  A  E  M  L  T  H  E  M  X  F  I  D  I
I  T  M  T  P  I  O  Z  L  B  G  R  U  N  N
N  T  D  T  O  G  W  G  U  A  R  D  I  N  G
G  E  I  E  S  H  N  E  O  L  O  G  I  S  M
C  R  K  D  E  T  A  R  E  C  R  A  C  N  I
```

ABODES	FIGHTERS	PLUMBING
ASSUREDLY	FUNKY	POTTER
BESTOW	GUARDING	SATYR
CAPITALS	INCARCERATED	SKYLIGHT
CHAPEL	MIDWIFES	SURVEY
COUPING	MINIATURIZED	TARNISHING
DISCOMPOSE	MODIFICATIONS	TERRORS
DUSTIEST	NEOLOGISM	TOILETTE

Assorted Words 35

```
Y P G R E I L E P A H S A T R
Q C R T N A S S I O R C Q H U
S T N E M P R A C S E Y K R N
C K X K A R T I E S T E O O D
Q I N T E R R O G A T I O N O
G D X B U I L D U P S D P G W
D O E R S S E N R E G A E I N
U F H Y H E R N I A G A B N S
T N A R I P S A P F J V N G W
N A M W O H S B I N D O O R A
G A Y E S T D E V O R P E R D
X R O D G N I T S I E H Z M I
E C Y Q A F A C E L I F T S E
A L U O R T S E I F F U R C S
X Y L C R O S S I N G E N A C
```

ARTIEST	FACELIFTS	SCRUFFIEST
ASPIRANT	GAYEST	SHAPELIER
BUILDUPS	HEISTING	SHOWMAN
CROISSANT	HERNIA	THRONGING
CROSSING	INDOOR	WADIES
DOERS	INTERROGATION	
EAGERNESS	REPROVED	
ESCARPMENTS	RUNDOWNS	

Assorted Words 36

```
F  E  S  S  E  N  I  T  L  I  U  G  Y  A  U
Y  R  A  C  I  V  A  Q  E  Z  I  L  Y  T  S
S  T  N  A  I  G  G  P  U  A  J  C  O  C  H
P  N  S  R  E  G  N  A  D  A  E  F  P  P  E
E  N  E  R  G  I  Z  E  D  A  I  M  A  I  R
R  U  D  B  I  C  B  Q  F  Q  E  N  D  M  L
I  U  B  O  C  H  L  A  F  S  O  D  T  P  M
S  C  L  W  M  S  T  N  E  I  L  A  S  R  O
H  D  D  L  Z  I  H  D  E  P  L  O  R  E  D
I  M  L  E  B  A  C  H  O  R  N  F  A  S  E
N  X  M  R  N  O  B  I  I  O  J  M  S  S  R
G  B  X  S  F  N  Q  E  L  U  L  X  K  I  N
S  E  C  I  R  F  I  T  N  E  D  B  X  N  I
S  E  I  D  R  A  T  B  E  H  I  N  D  G  T
V  M  Z  I  K  C  A  B  S  A  V  N  A  C  Y
```

BEHIND	DEPLORED	QUAINT
BINNED	DOMICILE	SALIENTS
BLOODTHIRSTY	ENERGIZED	STYLIZE
BOWLERS	GIANTS	TARDIES
CANVASBACK	GUILTINESS	USHER
DANGERS	IMPRESSING	VICAR
DEADPAN	MODERNITY	
DENTIFRICES	PERISHING	

Assorted Words 37

```
Y  B  B  R  E  F  E  R  E  N  D  U  M  S  C
R  E  O  J  Y  C  N  A  N  G  I  L  A  M  M
W  I  R  R  I  G  A  T  E  D  H  D  R  I  A
C  A  O  E  R  E  S  P  A  W  N  S  T  I  G
E  O  I  Y  T  I  M  E  R  T  X  E  A  U  D
S  L  N  L  R  A  W  K  I  G  A  P  I  N  R
H  F  T  F  S  C  G  D  D  B  G  N  K  R  G
R  B  A  T  I  N  G  E  R  U  B  Q  X  W  F
I  R  H  N  A  R  E  I  L  D  D  U  C  Z  L
V  O  E  Y  T  R  M  O  T  E  H  K  H  H  B
E  S  D  K  F  I  K  E  G  Q  D  J  U  Q  T
L  U  K  N  C  Z  C  Q  D  M  P  V  P  N  V
L  D  O  R  K  I  E  S  T  F  E  J  P  H  N
E  S  E  A  L  A  S  P  L  E  N  A  R  Y  R
D  M  K  K  L  I  Q  U  I  D  A  T  O  R  I
```

ANTICS	GNASH	REFERENDUMS
BATING	HUBBIES	SHRIVELLED
CONFIRMED	IRRIGATED	SICKER
CUDDLIER	LIQUIDATOR	WAILS
DELEGATE	MALIGNANCY	
DORKIEST	PAWNS	
EXTREMITY	PLENARY	
FRIEND	RATTLE	

Assorted Words 38

```
H  E  E  D  L  E  S  S  N  E  S  S  I  G  I
D  K  Y  S  D  R  S  W  A  J  A  X  M  R  N
A  L  Y  R  T  E  E  U  M  E  J  J  P  R  S
H  L  R  L  T  A  H  D  O  E  P  H  R  O  E
U  D  L  E  L  E  R  S  N  R  U  I  E  U  M
P  G  U  I  F  A  G  R  A  E  A  V  S  N  I
S  H  F  H  D  U  C  D  I  W  M  C  S  D  N
T  E  C  I  F  E  L  I  A  E  N  R  I  H  A
A  M  S  L  R  Y  C  G  R  G  R  U  O  O  T
G  L  G  N  R  E  Y  L  E  Y  P  I  N  U  I
E  I  B  J  E  X  S  K  F  N  L  S  I  S  N
D  N  I  D  U  P  L  I  C  A  T  E  S  E  G
L  E  P  H  B  A  X  M  D  O  X  R  T  S  C
Y  R  O  I  R  P  J  E  B  E  T  S  R  U  C
Z  C  I  B  M  A  I  S  R  Z  S  S  M  M  C
```

CAROUSE	HEEDLESSNESS	REFULGENT
CEDILLA	HEMLINE	ROUNDHOUSES
CRUISERS	IAMBIC	STARRIER
CUTELY	IMPRESSIONIST	STOCKY
DUPLICATE	INSEMINATING	UNWASHED
EXPENSES	LYRICALLY	UPSTAGED
FIRESIDES	MENDER	
GADGETRY	PRIORY	

Assorted Words 39

```
C  G  A  M  B  O  L  L  I  N  G  B  Z  Y  N
F  I  N  A  N  C  E  D  L  W  P  S  I  L  E
X  T  W  I  R  R  E  F  U  T  A  B  L  E  R
P  S  S  Q  T  I  G  G  A  S  D  J  T  N  V
B  T  T  I  D  C  H  N  Y  X  I  D  A  G  O
T  E  S  S  S  S  I  E  I  T  S  R  S  T  U
D  S  T  E  E  N  N  D  J  R  T  B  T  H  S
W  E  E  T  B  R  O  A  D  S  E  D  E  I  N
D  G  D  S  O  R  E  C  P  A  N  K  R  L  E
O  K  N  U  U  R  E  T  R  H  D  P  C  Y  S
F  T  R  I  R  T  S  P  N  E  S  P  O  I  S
N  A  E  R  P  T  B  R  U  I  P  I  Z  Y  B
S  P  O  U  T  A  N  O  P  S  S  U  D  R  O
F  C  S  V  H  T  E  I  T  H  G  I  E  T  H
S  N  E  R  V  E  S  L  G  V  U  Y  D  W  V
```

ADDICTING	EIGHTIETH	NERVOUSNESS
BETTORS	FINANCED	OBTUSEST
BICKERING	GAMBOLLING	SPOUT
BROADS	INTRUDED	SUPERBEST
CONSIST	IRREFUTABLE	TASTER
DISHPANS	LEAPING	
DISINTERESTS	LENGTHILY	
DISTENDS	NERVES	

Assorted Words 40

```
D  T  S  M  S  N  D  O  L  M  E  N  P  H  Q
V  E  S  B  C  E  E  E  S  B  Q  I  U  U  I
C  S  R  I  I  T  I  H  P  E  X  Z  Z  N  N
S  S  R  E  N  R  S  D  C  P  C  X  A  K  C
D  N  M  E  T  R  E  S  O  T  O  A  L  E  U
S  E  O  S  U  R  E  O  E  B  I  H  T  R  R
M  L  L  O  I  Q  A  T  G  L  Y  K  C  I  I
O  E  A  B  B  C  C  B  N  H  E  S  K  N  O
N  V  R  G  B  A  R  A  X  I  C  V  U  G  U
K  T  L  E  E  I  B  O  L  V  X  R  O  B  S
E  I  D  M  S  R  N  K  X  J  U  O  U  L  V
Y  N  S  V  P  C  O  R  S  E  T  E  D  H  V
E  G  F  B  T  N  E  I  C  I  F  F  E  O  C
D  E  T  I  E  F  O  R  E  S  T  E  R  S  H
C  S  R  L  C  I  M  R  E  D  O  P  Y  H  W
```

BABOONS	EXORCISMS	LOVELESS
BARTERED	FORESTER	MERES
BUSYBODIES	HUNKERING	MONKEYED
CHOPPED	HYPODERMIC	NIBBLED
CHURCHGOER	INCURIOUS	REGALS
COEFFICIENT	INTERNIST	TACES
CORSETED	KITCHEN	TINGES
DOLMEN	LACQUERS	

Assorted Words 41

```
Y  D  S  E  Z  I  S  A  H  P  M  E  D  D  L
W  D  J  A  G  X  L  E  F  E  T  I  S  H  I
N  N  D  V  D  A  P  I  L  A  C  J  E  U  A
H  U  D  O  R  R  R  Z  Q  B  I  V  R  C  B
E  J  J  N  W  E  E  N  H  U  B  R  V  F  I
C  F  G  H  E  S  W  U  E  K  I  I  E  Z  L
M  C  O  N  S  C  I  O  U  S  L  Y  R  S  I
U  Y  E  F  I  E  S  N  P  D  G  R  S  D  T
S  D  L  M  Y  L  R  A  G  G  E  B  B  H  I
I  K  E  D  L  B  E  V  N  N  S  O  C  R  E
C  V  V  C  Q  L  Z  S  I  E  I  H  O  V  S
I  A  E  Y  E  C  Y  N  I  C  T  P  H  C  U
A  A  N  O  X  I  C  G  D  H  E  I  R  U  P
N  N  S  L  A  I  V  I  R  T  C  S  H  A  I
S  K  N  O  B  B  I  E  S  T  G  R  B  W  H
```

ASCEND	DRIBBLES	LIABILITIES
BEGGARLY	ELEVENS	MUSICIANS
CHISELING	EMPHASIZES	SERVERS
CONSCIOUSLY	ENRAGE	SERVICES
COOED	FAIREST	TRIVIAL
CYNIC	FETISH	WHITEN
DECEIVE	HARPING	
DOWSING	KNOBBIEST	

Assorted Words 42

```
O W S A R D Y H H O G W A S H
N V C G G C E M D K S P N C R
E S O Y J A D T U I D P I J Y
A Q N N T L R E C E T E M F Y
B I V I V I E D I E C C T I I
R J O P A S N P E F L Y H P P
S O Y T P T B E A N I P L E O
H F S E R H N L M H I M M A D
A F S N I E C O O A C N M O A
R I A Y C N H H C O T V G U C
M C B B E I A M T B D B G B M
O E G O S C N O C A R I N A N
N S H T E I T H G I E J E H U
I I X C A R E L E S S N E S S
C O U N T E R P A N E Y K J I
```

AMENITY
BLOODIES
CALISTHENIC
CARELESSNESS
CHANTER
CHAPEL
COMPLECTED
CONTAINS

CONVOYS
COUNTERPANE
DITCHED
EIGHTIETHS
GARDENING
HARMONIC
HOGWASH
HYDRAS

LYCEUM
MUMMIFIED
OCARINA
OFFICES
OPTED
PIMPS
PRICES

Assorted Words 43

```
Y  X  C  A  K  I  S  U  O  I  R  E  P  M  I
K  U  F  O  O  G  N  I  Y  E  B  O  S  I  D
L  F  V  S  L  T  T  E  S  S  I  M  E  R  F
R  O  S  S  E  L  N  S  L  L  L  V  G  H  P
F  L  E  R  T  B  E  E  E  E  F  I  N  K  R
S  U  Q  O  N  A  G  C  M  I  G  Y  G  A  I
T  T  R  H  L  U  T  N  T  R  F  A  N  Q  V
L  F  J  N  I  D  Q  B  I  I  E  F  N  R  A
E  T  E  P  I  S  E  U  L  R  V  T  A  C  T
H  I  A  T  U  S  D  R  O  G  E  I  T  D  E
Q  Q  K  L  E  U  H  D  O  O  N  T  S  E  F
S  E  V  I  E  C  R  E  P  H  Z  I  T  T  B
S  K  I  T  I  N  G  N  D  M  C  I  R  U  S
D  V  S  S  C  I  T  O  R  U  E  N  N  A  B
V  T  L  O  A  F  E  D  A  H  L  I  A  G  R
```

ANCHORED	DISOBEYING	NEUROTICS
BAUDS	FURNISHED	OOZING
BETTERMENT	HIATUS	PERCEIVES
BURDEN	IMPERIOUS	PRIVATE
BUTTERING	INELEGANCE	RARING
COLLECTIVISTS	KNIFE	REMISS
DAFFIEST	LESSOR	SKITING
DAHLIA	LOAFED	

Assorted Words 44

```
L  E  T  A  I  R  U  X  U  L  J  X  G  H  N
D  O  K  L  A  I  N  N  E  L  L  I  M  H  Y
G  M  S  I  N  O  I  S  S  E  R  P  M  I  S
U  Q  J  E  M  A  N  C  I  P  A  T  E  S  J
X  P  E  G  O  G  A  M  E  D  E  P  O  D  Z
H  R  D  G  R  E  N  X  C  R  A  C  K  E  R
A  O  A  E  N  E  Z  I  S  R  T  Z  Y  W  U
L  M  M  V  F  I  S  A  T  E  A  I  K  W  O
F  E  N  W  I  A  R  P  E  O  R  L  F  A  G
P  N  A  P  N  P  M  E  I  L  O  O  L  Y  R
E  A  B  G  R  P  E  A  G  R  S  H  N  I  A
N  D  L  D  Q  T  W  R  T  N  A  P  S  S  P
N  E  E  J  Y  L  L  A  N  O  I  T  O  M  E
Y  G  N  I  N  R  A  E  L  E  R  F  O  R  S
B  S  G  Y  N  E  C  O  L  O  G  Y  F  R  P
```

CERTIFY	FINGERING	PROMENADE
CRACKER	GRAPES	PROPS
DAMNABLE	GYNECOLOGY	RELEARNING
DEFAMATORY	HALFPENNY	RESPIRATOR
DEMAGOG	IMPRESSIONISM	SHOOTING
DOPED	LUXURIATE	SLEAZE
EMANCIPATES	MILLENNIAL	SNORES
EMOTIONALLY	PILLAR	VIPER

Assorted Words 45

```
T  O  Q  D  S  E  I  K  O  O  R  N  Q  O  R
S  T  E  E  P  L  E  J  A  C  K  B  A  S  H
G  D  N  S  D  E  A  D  L  I  E  R  L  K  A
W  C  E  H  G  M  O  N  I  T  O  R  S  X  P
P  M  O  B  E  N  G  S  I  T  U  A  T  E  S
L  O  O  L  R  A  I  K  M  G  G  M  I  U  O
U  W  M  O  L  I  D  W  T  G  I  I  X  S  D
M  H  A  U  C  O  E  S  O  S  T  R  C  V  I
E  D  D  V  U  H  I  F  T  R  E  V  O  C  Z
S  K  D  C  R  E  E  D  S  O  C  G  M  B  E
M  G  E  R  S  C  C  R  Q  X  N  Q  I  H  A
D  I  S  C  O  M  M  O  D  E  R  E  M  D  J
R  E  T  T  R  W  D  E  S  U  R  E  D  N  U
S  G  V  S  E  U  G  O  G  A  D  E  P  G  C
Y  N  U  M  S  K  U  L  L  S  I  J  N  K  P
```

ABORIGINALS	DIGEST	PLUMES
COLLOID	DISCOMMODE	RHAPSODIZE
COVERT	HEADSTONE	ROOKIES
CREEDS	MADDEST	SITUATE
CROWING	MONITORS	STEEPLEJACK
CURSORES	MOOCHER	UNDERUSED
DEADLIER	NUMSKULLS	
DEBRIEFS	PEDAGOGUES	

Assorted Words 46

```
S  L  M  I  S  C  A  R  R  I  A  G  E  S  Y
A  S  N  O  I  T  I  N  U  M  F  P  B  E  M
P  P  E  F  I  L  T  R  A  T  I  N  G  K  O
M  M  T  S  E  I  C  N  A  F  S  F  G  I  X
D  W  T  N  A  H  C  R  E  M  L  K  G  N  Y
W  E  F  C  E  M  M  T  E  L  T  N  U  A  G
D  D  K  O  O  S  A  E  C  I  U  L  S  D  E
M  E  E  R  Z  M  S  L  I  O  M  W  J  V  N
R  O  L  T  O  D  M  A  L  F  R  M  Q  I  A
O  Z  I  I  R  W  L  A  P  O  G  C  L  S  T
M  A  S  S  M  O  R  E  N  S  C  L  S  A  I
P  C  K  O  T  I  S  E  I  D  Z  A  W  B  N
E  S  K  N  Y  E  T  F  V  F  E  G  T  L  G
R  C  K  E  L  Z  N  E  Z  O  N  R  D  E  H
S  S  N  W  O  D  B  U  R  W  H  I  S  D  M
```

ALLOCATE
APTNESS
COMMANDERS
CORTISONE
DELIMITER
FANCIEST
FILTRATING
GAUNTLET

INADVISABLE
INFIELD
MERCHANT
MISCARRIAGES
MOISTEN
MUNITIONS
OVERWORKED
OXYGENATING

ROMPERS
RUBDOWNS
SLUICE
SORTED

Assorted Words 47

```
N  N  I  R  E  C  Y  L  G  O  R  T  I  N  O
L  K  F  K  E  P  I  S  T  A  C  H  I  O  S
Q  N  O  I  T  A  L  E  R  R  O  C  V  B  G
N  O  I  T  A  R  O  P  R  O  C  P  G  O  O
C  L  L  S  N  O  I  T  A  C  I  R  B  A  F
R  C  E  D  E  N  E  V  A  R  T  N  O  C  F
A  S  D  R  E  H  P  A  R  G  O  M  E  D  H
F  L  A  I  C  O  S  A  D  N  E  B  N  U  Z
T  W  U  P  G  H  S  I  K  C  A  L  B  E  L
I  H  D  E  Y  A  R  G  N  I  R  I  A  H  C
N  R  D  O  L  L  Y  H  P  O  R  O  L  H  C
E  S  E  R  O  F  A  N  I  P  M  F  B  S  D
S  O  B  O  U  T  E  R  S  Q  E  D  M  F  A
S  E  T  A  C  I  T  N  E  H  T  U  A  T  I
P  H  R  F  O  N  D  N  E  S  S  A  G  C  X
```

ADMONISHES	CORRELATION	NITROGLYCERIN
ASOCIAL	CRAFTINESS	OUTERS
AUTHENTICATES	DEMOGRAPHER	PINAFORES
BLACKISH	DRUID	PISTACHIOS
CHAIRING	FABRICATIONS	UNBEND
CHLOROPHYLL	FOILED	
CONTRAVENED	FONDNESS	
CORPORATION	GRAYED	

Assorted Words 48

```
S  R  C  A  T  A  W  D  R  I  N  E  S  S  L
F  X  E  Y  R  N  O  C  L  A  F  E  B  A  B
L  H  R  E  L  C  G  L  X  N  J  K  S  Y  A
O  O  I  F  N  D  G  N  I  R  R  A  M  T  J
C  B  S  A  Q  A  E  D  I  B  L  E  I  E  L
K  O  E  M  I  D  C  T  F  P  V  M  R  M  I
S  E  M  U  S  N  O  C  A  L  A  I  K  B  B
M  D  S  G  N  B  P  I  U  L  N  R  A  L  E
W  I  G  E  O  N  S  K  L  B  E  Y  G  O  R
H  A  R  P  O  O  N  E  D  I  F  B  R  R  A
T  S  E  R  U  C  S  B  O  Z  E  E  W  S  T
V  I  X  N  B  E  F  E  N  C  E  S  H  Z  I
S  D  I  A  M  D  N  A  H  V  K  F  L  P  O
N  P  E  R  S  U  A  S  I  V  E  Z  X  U  N
Y  A  D  R  E  S  T  R  I  C  T  I  V  E  S
```

BELATEDLY	FLOCKS	OBSCURES
BUCCANEER	GOOSE	PERSUASIVE
CERISE	GRAPING	RESTRICTIVES
CONSUMES	HANDMAIDS	SMIRK
DOILIES	HARPOONED	TAWDRINESS
EDIBLE	HOBOED	TEMBLOR
FALCONRY	LIBERATION	WIGEONS
FENCES	MARRING	

Assorted Words 49

```
C  V  K  O  E  B  D  E  H  T  U  O  M  M  Z
Z  I  Y  F  P  A  C  O  U  N  T  E  S  S  L
H  T  D  S  Y  R  R  T  T  A  S  B  H  B  V
V  G  Q  E  F  R  N  A  W  O  R  K  O  U  T
A  S  S  U  R  E  S  A  C  S  O  N  V  J  R
K  O  A  R  E  T  I  M  H  H  Q  V  E  H  U
L  C  K  G  R  T  I  L  U  K  E  U  D  U  A
I  U  E  B  T  E  S  H  E  I  A  L  I  E  N
A  C  C  E  P  T  I  N  G  B  N  R  S  R  T
X  S  N  A  K  E  S  G  O  S  V  A  T  E  E
A  S  E  I  R  U  C  P  G  O  T  L  R  S  D
X  O  H  G  M  A  H  T  E  O  L  R  L  E  A
E  Z  O  V  S  T  C  I  V  E  M  L  A  P  G
N  T  S  E  I  C  E  E  L  F  Q  S  A  P  V
C  O  M  P  U  T  E  R  I  Z  E  S  B  B  S
```

ACCEPTING	COMPUTERIZES	SHOVED
ASSURES	COUNTESS	SMOGGIER
ASTRAKHAN	CURIES	SNAKES
BALLOONS	EARACHE	SQUIRE
BARRETTE	EVICTS	STRAPS
BELIEFS	FLEECIEST	TRUANTED
CARACUL	GERANIUMS	WORKOUT
CIDER	MOUTHED	

Assorted Words 50

```
G  L  R  S  O  M  A  N  I  F  E  S  T  S  J
X  T  A  G  R  Y  T  I  N  I  V  I  D  E  R
S  K  D  X  H  E  T  N  A  L  P  M  I  X  P
N  F  I  W  O  G  S  F  G  M  D  D  S  Q  O
O  Q  A  X  N  L  G  A  C  W  R  E  S  P  U
N  L  N  F  U  O  B  D  E  T  A  S  I  U  L
R  V  C  T  T  C  E  E  X  T  I  P  M  C  T
I  E  E  X  S  K  I  V  S  P  N  A  U  S  I
G  R  O  S  S  E  D  E  E  G  E  I  L  O  C
I  I  S  M  O  N  S  L  R  E  D  R  A  A  E
D  F  Y  T  X  S  H  O  R  E  R  I  T  R  D
K  I  N  R  Y  P  R  P  L  K  E  N  I  M  B
U  E  Y  L  D  I  V  I  L  C  L  G  N  P  T
L  S  M  K  L  E  N  N  L  C  I  L  G  F  C
S  E  S  E  Y  L  B  G  Y  W  F  Y  O  R  E
```

BRAINTEASERS	GROSSED	SHORE
CLOSEST	IMPLANT	STYING
DESPAIRINGLY	LIVIDLY	VERIFIES
DEVELOPING	MANIFESTS	YESES
DISSIMULATING	NONRIGID	
DIVINITY	POULTICED	
DRAINED	RADIANCE	
GLOCKENSPIEL	REEVE	

Assorted Words 51

```
Y  H  H  D  E  R  E  P  A  I  D  S  O  F  P
M  S  L  I  V  E  D  E  R  A  D  O  X  W  L
A  B  S  Y  D  Z  E  X  T  Y  C  P  U  P  E
R  H  C  E  C  E  T  A  L  O  I  V  N  I  A
A  C  S  A  N  U  M  N  G  T  O  G  V  T  S
T  G  P  Y  B  L  D  E  I  B  U  B  L  C  A
H  S  O  S  L  A  U  D  H  A  Y  L  G  H  N
O  E  I  A  N  L  L  F  L  C  P  N  T  F  T
N  T  L  T  E  U  U  K  H  I  S  E  O  O  E
E  E  E  D  A  A  G  F  I  T  E  I  R  R  R
R  A  R  I  R  M  Q  G  T  E  I  S  I  K  A
S  C  J  C  K  U  A  B  L  H  S  A  T  I  B
G  H  W  H  P  Q  C  R  I  I  G  T  F  M  D
S  N  I  K  S  G  I  P  D  A  N  I  K  W  A
B  T  Q  J  C  F  I  Z  Z  I  N  G  R  E  M
```

BALKIEST	FIZZING	SCHEMED
BOOTEE	INVIOLATE	SNUGGLING
CUDDLIEST	MARATHONERS	SPOILER
CURDLE	PIGSKINS	TEACH
DAREDEVIL	PITCHFORK	
DIAPERED	PLEASANTER	
DRAMATIST	REPAINT	
FAITHFULNESS	RIGHTFULLY	

Assorted Words 52

```
D  S  M  T  X  S  I  I  J  P  F  E  B  H  X
T  E  E  Y  G  O  L  O  C  A  M  R  A  H  P
C  I  M  T  S  M  I  A  L  C  C  A  V  V  U
P  I  Q  R  O  S  E  N  I  T  N  E  L  A  V
E  M  S  L  A  N  I  G  I  R  O  B  A  C  G
R  M  Z  N  H  W  K  R  O  W  G  E  L  C  Y
S  O  B  H  Z  O  G  N  I  L  L  E  U  R  G
U  R  I  G  N  I  N  I  A  R  T  S  E  R  L
A  T  F  T  E  U  Q  I  R  B  F  N  W  S  S
S  A  X  G  N  I  T  T  E  N  S  Z  E  Z  I
I  L  L  B  D  Y  L  M  O  D  N  A  R  P  X
O  I  N  N  I  J  G  N  I  D  U  O  R  H  S
N  Z  L  Q  P  E  R  S  P  E  C  T  I  V  E
S  E  E  Z  I  R  A  T  I  L  I  M  E  D  M
Z  D  E  I  F  I  T  N  E  D  I  S  I  M  W
```

ABORIGINALS	IMMORTALIZED	RANDOMLY
ACCLAIMS	JINNI	RESTRAINING
BANKNOTES	LEGWORK	SHROUDING
BRIQUET	MISIDENTIFIED	SPENT
CLAMP	NETTING	VALENTINES
DEMILITARIZE	PERSPECTIVE	WARMED
GRUELLING	PERSUASIONS	
HONIED	PHARMACOLOGY	

SUDOKU

Puzzle #1

medium

	3		8	2	6		1	9
7		6	3					
	2	8			7	3		
			6	9	3			5
6		2				1		
5			2					8
		9		5				
	5		1				3	4
		1			4	8		

60

Puzzle #2

medium

		4				8	6	
6	9		4		2	1		
				7	6			
				2	4	3		
1			3	6	9			2
7		2						6
								8
8	5		2	1	3		7	
	6		8	9		2		1

Puzzle #3

medium

					2	5	8	
		8	1		5			
6				9		4		
1			5				4	
5		4	3	2	9	6		
7	9					3		
	2			7	4			5
				6			9	
	4		9		3	2	7	6

Puzzle #4

medium

	2		6				8	4
		6		7		3	5	
	7			5		1		
		3	2					1
					8	5	9	
8					5	2	3	7
1			9		7			
	9	8	3	1	6			

Puzzle #5

medium

		8						
	3			1	5		8	
2					4		7	
						9	6	
	9		6	2		4	3	8
		7					1	
3		2			6	7	4	9
6			2		3		5	1
	1				9	3	2	

Puzzle #6

medium

				7	9		5	8
	3	6		4	8	1	2	
			6		1		4	
				8			7	5
5		2	1					9
3			4					
	5	8			2	7	6	1
7		9	8					
	1						9	

Puzzle #7

medium

			5			9		
		4		7	8	1	6	5
	1		9				8	
2		3				4		
5		8	6	9			7	
9	6				7			
				4		6	1	
	3					8	2	
4		7		1	6	3		

Puzzle #8

medium

7	8		6			9	3	
		1						7
2				9	1	8	6	
6	1		2					4
			8					
	9			3		6	1	
1				7			2	6
4		3		6			8	
	7	6			4		5	

Puzzle #9

medium

					1	7		2
	1		4		6			
	7	4	8	5		9		
			1				2	
	8	1			7	4		
	9	7	2	8	3		1	
	5	3						8
		9		3		1	5	
		6				2	3	

Puzzle #10

medium

9	2					6	4	1
	8	4						
		3	4		9	2		
					5	3	8	
2			8					4
		6	7	1	3			
4	5	9	3					
	7			6		8		
	6	8					3	2

Puzzle #11

medium

6							9					4
		3		4						9	6
						6				3		5
				8		5			4		9
4	2			9							
7				6						8	
5				1		4			9		
						6				4	8
1		4		8				6		7

Puzzle #12

medium

	1	5						6
6		7		5	2	1		
8				4			7	
		8						2
	2		5				6	7
3						8	4	5
		1		8		2		
5	9	6						4
2		3			5	6		

Puzzle #13

medium

2		4		8		5	3	
			5		4	1		
5	9	1	2					
		9	6	1				4
7		6				9		
4	5						7	
6	3					7		
	7				1			
		5	7				8	3

Puzzle #14

medium

	2							6
	5			9	3		7	8
8			7				3	
		4	9	6			1	
				4		6		
7	9		1			4	2	
9		2		1	6		8	5
1			8	3	9	7		
					5			4

Puzzle #15

medium

3			1				2	
		7	2	6		4		
	2	4		8	9		1	
		3					9	5
8				4	2	1		6
5				9			7	
9								2
	3				5	9	4	
7		5					6	

Puzzle #16

medium

3						6		5
		2					4	
6	9	5		1	2	7	3	
	5			2		4		
8			7				1	
1	2			3	4			
5		3		8	9		7	
		8						
2				4	3	8		6

Puzzle #17

medium

	8		9				2	
3				1	8	5	9	
5		7	3			1	6	8
4	1			2		8		
7		5			4			
	2	8				6		
	5						8	1
6	3				7			4
			1			2		

Puzzle #18

medium

	1				4	9	8	
9			6	7	1			3
	5		8	2			6	
1							7	
6			1		8			
		9		5	6			4
3							5	
8		1			5			
	7			8	2	3		

Puzzle #19

medium

		1	8					
		6			1		7	9
	7			6	2		5	
9	8				3	1		
3						5	9	4
1		5	6	4		3		
5			1	3				
	4	8			5			
		3	9				6	

Puzzle #20

medium

	5				8		1	
		7		2			6	
		3	9	6			5	2
	6		2			4		1
		2					3	9
				9		6		8
			7	5		1		
5	3					7		
9	7			4	3			

Puzzle #21

medium

	8		7			2		
	1	4	2			6		
2	3	9		8	6			4
5					4	7		3
			7					1
	9						6	
					8	5	4	
		6	1	2		9		7
	2		4					

80

Puzzle #22

medium

		8				9	4	3
		3	8					
9	2	7				8	6	
	9			8		1		
			4		6		2	5
2	7			3	5			
								4
3		5		4	7		8	
				1	8	3	7	9

Puzzle #23

medium

	5	4	9				6	1
7								
1				6		8		9
	2				9	5	3	
			6	1		9		
		9		5				
9	6	7	2				4	
	1		5		4	6		2
	4					3	8	

Puzzle #24

medium

		6			2	8	3	
7		3	4	6				2
2	5			3		4	6	
					7	1		8
	1	4				6		3
5							2	
							9	
		8	2		6	3		
9		2	3			7		

Puzzle #25

medium

7	3					8	4	
	9			6				
	5	2	9			7		6
9						1		
6				7		5		
	4	5	2					
							7	2
	8	7		2	3	4	9	1
2	6				1			8

Puzzle #26

medium

	4				7	5		
		7		5				6
	2		9	1				7
		2			6		5	1
	9				2	3		8
				8		7	9	
					1			
7		4	2		5			
5	1		8	6	9	2		

Puzzle #27

medium

	9			3		7		4
1			7		8	6		
3		6	2		4	8		9
								7
2			9		6		8	
6	1	9		8			2	
		4				1		
		1	8		2	5		
			5			2	9	

Puzzle #28

medium

			1	5				9
		5			2		8	4
1			8		9	3		
3	4	9		8	1	5		
8		1						7
				9	4			
	1			6			2	8
		4			3	7		1
		7						5

Puzzle #29

medium

			5		3			7
	8			6		2		3
	5			8		9	4	
			9			5	8	4
9		5			1			
8	7	4	3					
1			2	3				
	6							9
2	9			7				8

Puzzle #30

medium

		6		9			4	1
	5	9				3	8	2
	3	4				9	7	
5								
		8	1	2		4	3	
3	9				7			8
9	6			8	3	1	2	
	8			5			6	
		5	2					3

89

Puzzle #31

medium

		3				5		2
	2	1	4		6			
		6	8			1		4
	4	5	2	9		7	8	
		7		4		6		9
			7		5			
	5	8	9			3		
		2		3		9		
3	9						1	

Puzzle #32

medium

8	9			7		1	5	3
2	3						6	
5								8
	4							
			9		8	7		
		3			2			4
	1	7	6	2				
			8	5			7	
9		8	7	3				6

Puzzle #33

medium

	6							1
	5	7			1		2	
	2	3	8		5	9		
2		8	7	3				
4		9				6	7	
	7	6	2			8	1	
				4				
		2	1		7			
		1	6				3	4

Puzzle #34

medium

		9				4		3
			9	2				7
6			8	3	4		2	
	5		6	9				
4	8	2				6	3	
			3					2
9			2	1			7	
	1		4					
7	4			8			9	1

Puzzle #35

medium

	2		1		4		5	7
				6		1		2
		9					4	
1		8		7	5			
4	3		6					9
		2		3				1
5	7		9		6		8	
				5	2	7		
	6		8			9	3	

Puzzle #36

medium

	5	2			6			
	4						6	8
8				5		2	4	
		5	7	6				
	8			3	4			
	3	7					8	
5		4	3	8	7		1	9
				9		4	7	
	7	9			1		3	

Puzzle #37

medium

	2			9		3	4	
		8						7
4		1				5		
8			5	4	2		1	
5	7				1	4		3
2			7		6			9
			4			6		
9	6		2		8			
	4						7	

Puzzle #38

medium

	3		4	2	7			
	1	7		9	8			2
9				6	3			
2	5				4	1	6	
			1	2		8		3
	9		8					
		2	7			9	1	
					1		3	8
			6	3		4		5

Puzzle #39

medium

			9			6		
3		8		1	2	9	4	
	6	5		4		1	3	
1			3	5				
5	9				6		1	3
7			4					
			1			3		4
	2	7	8				6	
6	1						9	

Puzzle #40

medium

		3					9	
		2		4	3		8	6
			9			7		
2	8					3	1	7
				6		8		
9	5	7		3	8			2
1			7		9	2		4
5			3			9		
							6	

Puzzle #41

medium

4	1						8	
	7	2	8				5	
8	5				4	6		
	8	1					4	
			4		8	9	2	1
			7					
		8	9	3				7
6				4	7	2	9	
			5	8		4	3	

Puzzle #42

medium

		9	5	8	3			
		3		9	1			5
				2	4		3	
2		7	9	5	8		4	
			4				7	6
9						2		
4							6	
5		2	1	3		4		
		8		4		1		3

Puzzle #43

medium

1	7				2	5		
3			9				4	
		9		7		3	6	
5		2		6	1			7
4					3			9
8	6		7				2	
	3							5
9	5		1					
		4		8			1	

Puzzle #44

medium

9			2					
3	7		1		4	2		
6				3			5	1
	4				1		8	
		6				7		
2			8	6				9
8			5	4			6	3
	6	2						
	9	3			8	1	2	

Puzzle #45

medium

5				6			8	
			1					9
	4			7	8		3	6
	2	6	3	5	1	7		
		3					1	4
	8	7			6		5	
			4	1				
6			8		7		4	3
		4						

Puzzle #46

medium

				6	8			9
		6	5	9		2	7	
	4				2			
4	1		7	3				
3	9		8	1	5			
		8	9			3		7
2	3	1		4		8	9	
8	6			5	1			3

Puzzle #47

medium

5	6			3					
				6			2	8	
9				2		5				1
3	2	9				1				
6	4			5	7	3		9		
						9		6		
7		6				2		4	3	
		1							7	
	3					6				

Puzzle #48

medium

9	1		6		8	3	4	
	3			5		6		
7		6				5		
8		2	7					
1	6				4			
	9		3			2		
	8							3
			8	9	6	4		
6		9		4			1	2

Puzzle #49

medium

	2						7	3
6	9		3			8		
		1		7	8		6	
7					2	1		5
2			6		1	3		
			7	4				
	1				7			
8		6		1			9	
	7	4		5		2		8

Puzzle #50

medium

	7	4				9		
5				4				
1	2		9	3	7			8
8						2	3	
6	5		4					
	3	9		2	8	1		
				9		8		
9		3	5	7		4	2	1
		7			1			

Puzzle #51

medium

					6		2	9
	5	6			7			
		9		4	5	7		
9		5	4		1			
		4		6	2			
	2						7	
5	6	8		2			3	
		7	9				1	6
1						8		4

Puzzle #52

medium

	5				7		8	
1			2			4	3	5
							2	
9			8	1				7
			5			3		4
5	2	3						8
8	6					9		
	9	1	6	8				
	3		4		5			1

WORD SEARCH SOLUTIONS

ASSORTED WORDS 1

S	G	N	I	S	U	F	C	I	D	A	R	O	P	S
S	R	D	H	P	A	R	G	O	T	U	A		R	
	M	E	M	A	L	F	N	I					U	
P	P	U	K	R	E	C	A	N	T				D	
I	R	C	I	C	O	N	V	I	C	T	E	D	E	P
N	E	I		R	A	S	E		T				N	E
P	H	N	S		A	H	E	L		U			T	R
R	I	G	C	R	S	L	W	C	K		N		L	F
I	S			R	E	E	O	H	I	C		I	Y	E
C	T				O	L	C	S	S	F	U		M	C
K	O				O	L	R		U	I	R			T
I	R				K	E	O		B	R	T	E		
N	I		D	R	A	W	R	E	T	F	A		O	S
G	C	T	C	A	R	T	E	R	D		N			T
	S	E	I	T	N	U	A	J			E			

ASSORTED WORDS 2

G				Y	T	S	A	H						
R		P			S			C	N				A	
O		S	A			E			R	O			G	
U		G	E	D		E	S		B	O	N		I	
C	E	C	N	A	R	D	N	I	H	O	B	N	T	
H	S	S	E	I	P	E	E	I	V		O	A	A	
E		I	N	Z	R	O	D	Y	L	O		Z	T	C
S		P	T	R	I	A	R	E	E	A	R		E	
		O		I	E	L	E	T	E	K	C	P	D	S
		T	K		H	T	A	P	P	M	N	S	M	
		A		N		C	N	R	P	U	E	O	E	I
		S	E	L	O	S	N	I	T	A	R	R	M	M
		H			B		O		N	S	P	S		
	S	U	O	I	R	E	S		R		E	I	L	
K	I	C	K	O	F	F			B		C	D	E	

ASSORTED WORDS 3

S	L	I	G	H	T	B	S	P	I	H	C	O	R	C	I	M
							D	E	K	O	O	R				
	E		C	H	U	M	O	N	G	O	U	S				
		I	G	O	C		T	N	E	I	C	N	A	Q		
H	I		C	N	L	O	B	U	F	F	I	N	G	U		
Y	E	N	T	N	I	E	M	G	N	I	K	I	L	I		
	C	R	F	E	E	N	S	E			R			N		
		N	I	L	L	B	R	L	L			E		T		
			E	T	U	N	M	O	A	Y		Y	S	E		
			D	A	E	I	U	C	W		E	O	S			
				N	G	N		C			L	B	S			
	Y	L	I	R	E	E	E	Z		N		I	B	E		
E	C	N	A	M	O	R	P		A		I	D	I	N		
		D	I	S	I	N	H	E	R	I	T	S	N	C		
	M	O	L	L	I	F	I	E	D			G	E			

ASSORTED WORDS 4

C	S	L	A	I	R	O	T	C	I	P				
E	A	Y	H	A	R	E	F	I	N	E	R	Y	O	
S	R	G	F	T	E	S	R	E	T	C	E	P	S	S
E		A	I	T	R	E	L	B	B	I	R	D	I	
C	K	G	N	C	A	E	W			R	M	T		
T		O	O	G	I	C	A	O		O	A	I		
I	P	D	D	V	S	L	O		F	R		U	T	N
N	R		E	E	N	S	I	N		T	K	T	T	G
C	A	E	L	R	M	O	I	O	A		E	E	E	
U	N		I		E	A	C	P	N	D		R	R	
B	K		G	M		B	N		P	S	O		I	S
A	S		H		Y		M	K		I	P	S	N	
T	T		T			T		U	C		N	M	G	
E	E		L			S		L	I		G	U		
D	R		Y	G	N	I	N	O	I	T	N	E	M	P

Puzzle # 5
ASSORTED WORDS 5

```
P . C S R E T I R W Y P O C
A . D O . . . N C
T . E N . D E T A I N E D
H R L G F . . . P I . P
E E I R . O . . T . M R
T S B E . . S . I . . E . B
I T E G N . D S V . . A H R R
C F R A . O . E I . . M . O E
. U A T . N B . T L . B M C B
B L T E . . O K I L S L A H E
. M I D . . . I E . A E I U L
. D O L D R U M S E . X Z R L
. . N L . . . . N H . E E E
C R I P P L E D . . E C S . D
. . . . A R C I N G T
```

Puzzle # 6
ASSORTED WORDS 6

```
. . P E N I S . S . . . F
G P U R I T A N F . R . . O
. N S E L D D U P F . E . R
. D I V E R G I N G O F N N
. . . T B . . . . P L . I
B A T T A L I O N . E A L C L
. . . . I O . . . C T . A
N O I T A L L O C . K T . T F
E S E . . . I P . E E . I
U M D T . . . C E D S . O
N . B N A . . . N R T . N
S . . A A R D E T R O S N O C
E . . S L E X T R I C A T E
N . . . S S P A S S A B L Y
T . . . Y I O W I N G E R
```

Puzzle # 7
ASSORTED WORDS 7

```
. R R . . E D . E . . M I
F . E E . G S L E N . . A M
Y R S I I S N T D T . . R P
. L A E T D L I N R F . Q E
. . S N C T O A D A U I . U T
. D . U K N I O O N R H G I U
. . E G O I E R M C E O . S O
G . . T N I N G G E R B N . U
L . . S I C C R S G A . G S
A . . . U T S E E . A H . I
D . . . D H U N V . R C
D S N I F F I R G L S I . A
E F A M I L I A R I Z E D . G
S M A L S L O B B E R
T P R O B O S C I S . F
```

Puzzle # 8
ASSORTED WORDS 8

```
. E . D E T S A B M A L . G
. S V B . F A M I S H E S E
. G T A A L D E R W O M A N
. S A E D B G . D . . V E
O C S S N E E N S . . W A R
C . R H . L G D L I . H R I
C S E O . C I Y S S P . O M C
I C E W . L N G C E . M L I A
D H C I . O S . H . U . E N L
E U H N . V . . T . G . T L
N S Y G . E O V E R S E A S Y
T S . S D R A Y N R A B . L
A I D I S C L A I M I N G . P
L N H U C K L E B E R R I E S
. G . . . G L A M O R O U S
```

Puzzle # 9
ASSORTED WORDS 9

S	E	Z	I	C	I	T	I	L	O	P	E	D		
C			I	M	P	R	O	V	E	S				
S	O		S	L	A	T	N	E	M	A	D	N	U	F
	T	C			S	R	O	R	R	O	H			
	N	K		G	N	I	T	N	U	P		G		
M	S		I	S	D	E	C	A	N	T	E	R		E
I	U		O	U	S			U			N			
N	B	H	E	R	N	C	S			M		S	E	
E	C	E	B	R	E	A	K	A	B	L	E	M	C	R
R	U	E		U	K	D	E	P				O	I	
A	L	H		S	C	E	R	M			O	C		
L	T	A		S	A	U	S	O		P				
O	U	W		I	R	R		C	S					
G	R	E	T	R	E	A	D	S	F	C	T			
Y	E	D	I	N	V	E	S	T	I	T	U	R	E	S

Puzzle # 10
ASSORTED WORDS 10

E	T	I	R	W	R	E	V	O			S	C		
A	S	Y	A	W	T	R	A	P		N		N	I	
S	M	U		S			M	B			I	I	C	
Y	E	B	O	D	S			O				F	A	
P	L	T	I	M	E	E		B	L			F	T	T
L	M	S	A	T	E	N	N	B		D		L	R	Y
A		A	U	I	I	H	O	I	H		S	E	I	R
I		R	O	D	O	P	E	S	S		S	X	A	
T		T	E	E	U	S	G	S	I		E	N		
S			D	M	S	A	N	O	L	S	T			
D	E	T	A	R	E	B	I	L	L	U	L	W	S	
Y	T	I	V	A	C		H		Y	B	D	G	O	
P	U	S	S	I	E	R	M	E	A	T	B	A	L	L
	Y	L	B	A	R	O	L	P	E	D				
B	R	U	S	Q	U	E	N	E	S	S				

Puzzle # 11
ASSORTED WORDS 11

	P	R	O	P	E	L	L	E	D					
		R	O	R	G	A	N	I	S	M	S			
		N	E	S	T	L	I	N	G					
	T		D	M	E	T	A	B	O	L	I	S	M	
P	R	E	M	I	S	E	T		B			S		
S	A	S		C		R		O		O		L		
I	I	T		T		D	E		I		N	A		
X	L	A		S		E	I	R		L	S	U		
T	I	T		S		D	T	S	A	S	G			
I	N	E		H		E	I	P	E	O	H			
E	G	S	D	E	T	A	M	K	C	E	H	C	M	T
T		M		C		V	N	N				E		
H	E	A	D	H	U	N	T	E	R	A	I	S	R	
S		N		E		D	L	E	E					
			R	E	I	F	O	O	G	F	D			

Puzzle # 12
ASSORTED WORDS 12

		R	E	T	N	E	I	C	N	A				
	S		Y	P	I	N	S	T	R	I	P	E	S	
	I		L	O	C	O	W	E	E	D				
P	M			S		D		E						
Y	P	L		S		E		T	P					
R	L	S	I	P	E	E	D	N	M	H	R			
O	I	P	D	V	E	M	L	E	I	O	E			
T	S	A	P	R	G	E	R	I	T	T	P	M		
E	T	S	R	U	A	N	R	S	T	R	T	P	O	I
C	I	T	E	S	C	I	Y	U	T	A	I	E		
H	C	S	P	R	T	N	A	H	N	M	R			
N	O	E	S	R	S	G	E							
I	A	S	V	O	A	I	I	D						
C	C	E	O	P	E	O	N							
	R	A	S	H	E	R	S	N						

Puzzle # 13
ASSORTED WORDS 13

```
 G     T   R E I K R U M
   N   I N V I G O R A T E
 L G I     A B P U M P K I N
 E   N H   R A C R E A G E
 A C O M I C S G G L
         L T G N I D D E B
 H     D   E I   I M N
 E R I D D E D H W R P M E
 R C O L O R F A S T E P I S
 Y         F U   G A   S
 K I D D Y I N G U   B   N C
           H E R N I A A
 D E L O D       G     M
   D E N O U N C I N G
 G N I T C A T N O C
```

Puzzle # 14
ASSORTED WORDS 14

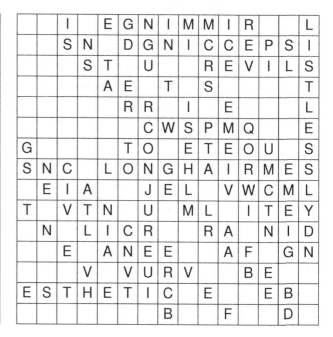

```
   I   E G N I M M I R     L
   S N   D G N I C C E P S I
     S T   U     R E V I L S
     A E   T   S         T
     R R   I   E         L
     C W S P M Q         E
 G     T O   E T E O U   S
 S N C   L O N G H A I R M E S
   E I A   J E L   V W C M L
 T V T N   U   M L   I T E Y
   N   L I C R   R A   N I D
   E   A N E E   A F   G N
     V   V U R V   B E
 E S T H E T I C   E     E B
         B   F     D
```

Puzzle # 15
ASSORTED WORDS 15

```
 D E L P M I S D T N E V E R P
   C U R T S E Y E D
 E       D   S G         L
   R F   M O D E L A R     I
 G N I R O S R U C   N A   C
 L   X F L I N E A L   N D K
 O   A   E S     R A   E E I
 N   T     S   E     E I   H N
 G   I     A   I     B M   G
 H   V   S N M E D N O C M E S
 O P E R J U R Y C   M     U D
 R   D E K C A B H C N U H   N
 N D I S T A S T E F U L L Y
 S     I M M U T A B L Y   A
 F I L C H I N G N I D O O W C
```

Puzzle # 16
ASSORTED WORDS 16

```
 D N U O P X E     B
 I   M O U S I N G   O   E
 S   C   Y T N A R A U G X
 O G O     L B     N   P   O
 R F N   S D A E H H C A E B B
 D O F I     B S   A E P C E S
 E U U   L   Y   E I S O T T O
 R L S     T S   R P T O R L
 L I T       I   T E T R A E
 Y O   S   T H   I E E A Y S
   N       I T C G D R T A C
   S       E     H E I L E
           R H   T D N N   N
     R O S I C N I G G     T
 S P A C I D N A H
```

Puzzle # 17
ASSORTED WORDS 17

D	A		S	C	O	M	P	E	L	L	E	D		
R	E	N		E	O						L			
A	N	F	A		R	L					A	R		
C	E	P	A	C		U	O	M	U	M	M	E	R	S
C	W	C	O	U	H	A	T	N			E	S		N
O	S		O	M	L	R	B	R	I		N	T		O
O	P			N	P	T	O	S	U	Z	T	O	B	O
N	A		E		S	A	E	N	C	N	E	C	O	P
S	P		M			E	D	D	I	O	D	K	N	I
T	E	D	E	K	O	V	N	O	C	S	N	E	G	E
A	R		N				T	U	D	M	D	O	S	
T	E		D				I	R	E	S	S	T		
I	D	E	M	O	L	I	T	I	O	N	E	D		
O	W	E	A	K	E	S	T	E	E	R	G	D	I	
N		S	E	T	A	M	I	T	S	E			S	

Puzzle # 18
ASSORTED WORDS 18

I			D	D	E	N	O	U	E	M	E	N	T	S
	M	C		I	C	X	J		H	S	I	D	O	M
S	B	P	A		G	R	P	A	P					O
	E		R	M		I	A	E	U	R				R
	L	I	Y	I	P	R	T	W	C	N	O			D
	L	A	L	C	S	U	E	A	F	T	T	U		A
F	B		T	L	A	O	S	I	L	I	I	E	D	I
L	O		N	I	U	N	I	T	I	S	N	D	N	
I	Y	O	E	E	E	B	Q	M	N	H	Z	H	G	S
B		T	T	S	M	L	E	E	G	G	E			
E			B	I	R	A	L	D	N		I	D		
L		A	N	E	D	I	A	T		M				
L			L	G	V	N	H	N						
E		R	E	V	O	L	I	N	U		I			
R		J	A	I	L	E	R	S	L	I	F			

Puzzle # 19
ASSORTED WORDS 19

N	N			E			G		S	F	F	O	C	S
S	A	U				T	M	I	N	T	I	E	S	T
	I	I	R		M	A				I	Z	A	P	O	T
P		N	C	R	C	A	R	E	E	R	I	N	G	
I		S	F	I	E		S	B			E			
C	G	Q		U	R	V		T	E				G	
K	T	U			L	T	O			O	L			N
E	R	E	S		F	L	A	S	H	I	E	S	T	A
R	A	L		S		D	Y	P			D	C		
E	V	C		D	E	Y	E	B	O	S	I	D		
L	E	H		Y	R	T	E	M	E	L	E	T		
S	L	E			I	N	I	T	R	A	M			
	I	S	F	L	A	G	E	L	L	A	T	I	O	N
	N			I	D	I	O	T	I	C	A	L	L	Y
	G			S	E	S	A	E	R	C	N	A	P	

Puzzle # 20
ASSORTED WORDS 20

	D	E	Z	A	F	C								I
F		X					C	O	W	O	R	R	O	S	M
R		C					S	R	P					M
E	S	E	M	U	F			P	E	P				U
E	A	P	T					I	W	E			E	N
L	L	T		N				T	M	R			X	I
A	I	I	T	D	E	L	L	A	C	T	A	C	P	Z
N	P	O		R		M				E	N	A	E	
C	S	N		C	A		R				D	T	S	
I	T	A			H	C	S	E	D	I	M	O	R	B
N	I	L				O	T	U	T			I		
G	C	L				P	I	L	T			A		
	K	Y				P	O	L	E		T			
S	U	O	N	I	T	U	L	G	E	N	E	B	E	
S	R	E	L	Z	Z	U	G			R	S	N	S	

117

Puzzle # 21
ASSORTED WORDS 21

```
  G Y   M A S H E R
C G N L   S   N D H C O O M I
  A N I G   E   A E         L
  T L I T N   O   I P       L
M R C C Y C I D D C T E     N
A A   A U A U R I S O N E   E
U S     M L L D I S I N E T S
S H E   E A E N U P M G G S
O E     N V R T D O Q L   A E
L S L     I S A I R C N A   S
E   T   N L I S O O S I C
A     T C   E G   N L I   E
F I N I T E L Y F O   S L M
        S K       Y     Y
      F L O P H O U S E S
```

Puzzle # 22
ASSORTED WORDS 22

```
  R   C O M P O S I T I O N S
  L E G   S E I R A T O R   C
  I   D N   F R U I T F U L O
  N P   N I   L E G G I E R M
  O R T   E Z   K         M
Y L I R A R T I B R A     A
D E N   B   N L A   E     N
I U T     O   O A N   R   D
S M     R   C T N   B E
C B R E A K N E C K   U A   E
I   C O M B A T A N T R W R
P D E T A C E R P E D   B S
L P R O P R I E T O R S
E     S E N I W T R E T N I
S C I T S A I S E L C C E
```

Puzzle # 23
ASSORTED WORDS 23

```
  S   B     D E E C O R P W
S M   U C H   V       E R A
E A   G   I O   I     M O L
R R A G N   B N L     A H K
V T A I   I N O E     R I I
I E   N L   R O R S   K B N
C S   G S H   E S E T   I I G
I T       N A   T D A Y N T S
N R E D I W E D   L N N G I M
G   S N O I S S A P A A A O E
    G N I U E U Q     R N L
E V O K E R G O N O M I C G T
          E X T R U D I N G E
  R E S T I N G         R
      P A C D E R       S
```

Puzzle # 24
ASSORTED WORDS 24

```
H     H F S     D       P
I       S A A R   A     E
S P   D E S R R O M E   R
T   O I   I E K R S   L   C
O L   L   K G N E O I   A O
R N A U A S C H I N W V   Z L
I   A T   R U O T S   S   A
A S S E N D L O C E S   T
N     S C E   S N Y E E   I
S       A M N N E P N R   N
        T I O I G P S D G
S U B T I T L E R N P I O
G N I P P A W S C T E P D P
  D U P L I C A T E S I N
H O M O G E N E O U S D   P I
```

Puzzle # 25
ASSORTED WORDS 25

O	L	S	E	N	A	T	I	V	I	T	I	E	S
U		O		L	S	B	D	S					
T		L	V		O	I	R	E	N				
D	R	U	R	I		P	T	I	I	G			
I	E	B	D	E	N	S	E	I	Q	R	I		
S	F	I	D	I	N	G	E	M	T	U	A	L	
T	E	L	R	A	F	I	L	N	E	A	E	L	A
A	R	I	A	E	S	F	L	Y	O	N	P	T	A	M
N	E	T	C	Y	G	H	U	R		B	T	E	S	S
C	N	Y	H		K	N	I	S	I		Y	S	H	
E	D		M			S	I	N	I	A		Z		
	U	M	A	C	H	O	I	L	G	N	I	W	A	C
	M		S	E	S	I	A	R		N	G			L
S	L	A	N	I	C	I	D	E	M	U				
				P	R	O	U	D	L	Y				

Puzzle # 26
ASSORTED WORDS 26

	I	N	T	E	R	C	H	A	N	G	I	N	G	
	D	R	O	W	N	S	N	O	L	Y	N			P
Y	S	O	E	B	A	N	K	R	O	L	L	S		H
	C	E	R	T	L	L	S	L	A	P	P	E	D	I
H	A	S	K	A	E	I		A			W		L
O	A		P	S	I	D		G	N		A		A
V	U		O	A	E	E		N		B	X		N
E		L		C	P	S	S	O	M	R	W	B	T
R		E			S	M	T	U		E	I	U	H
C			D		I	O	N		E	N	S	R
O	R	E	I	K	C	U	L	P	C		Z	G	T	O
M			D	I	N	G	I	E	R	I	S	L	P
I	A	S	B	E	S	T	O	S		N		E	Y
N					E	F	F	I	G	Y	S		
G	S	T	S	I	N	O	I	T	R	O	T	X	E

Puzzle # 27
ASSORTED WORDS 27

S		J	U	D	G	I	N	G					M
	R			D	C	W	R	E	A	K	E	D	E
		E		S	E	O						F	N
R			T	S		R	R	N				E	S
I	O	C		S	S	L	E	E	S			S	W
M		T	O		K	E	I	G	F	E		T	E
B	R	C	U	N	D	C	N	M	N	F	N		I	A
E	E		R	B	F	R	U	H	B	I	I	T	V	R
C	C		A	I	I	A	H	S	O	T	D	E
I	E	A		N	P	R	D	U		I	S	S	L	D
L	P		T	T		P	T	E	G		L		Y
I	T			E		I	N	N	D		U	
T	O			R	R		E	O	T	U		M
Y	R			S		E			S	C	L	M
	G	R	A	P	E	F	R	U	I	T	S	Y

Puzzle # 28
ASSORTED WORDS 28

N		S	R	O	L	I	C	N	U	O	C		
A		E		E	H	I	S	T	R	I	O	N	I	C
R		U	S	T	S	I	M	R	O	F	N	O	C
C			Q	P	A	L	M	E	D				
I	O			S		R	O	B			S		
S	C	R	D	S	R	A		E	A		W		
S	H	O	E	N	E	M		S	M		O		
U	O	I	L	L	O	N		H	I	I	R		
S	U	S	L	B	I	N	F		M	E			
E	N	E	A	B	S	U		M	S				
S	D	L	R	I	L	R			O	T			
	K	N	U	C	K	L	E	I	N	U	E		C
R	E	P	U	T	I	N	G	R	E		P	R	
C	O	N	N	E	C	T	O	R	S	S		X	O
	I	N	V	I	D	I	O	U	S			E	F

119

Puzzle # 29
ASSORTED WORDS 29

S	R	E	K	N	A	T	S	M	R	E	T	D	I	M
D	E		S	U	B	S	I	D	I	N	G			C
T	I	G			D	E	T	C	I	V	E			O
O	M	S	A		B	A	C	K	L	O	G	S		N
L	L	A	D	W	G					R		M	T	
E	O		R	A	E	N	G	H			D	E	U	
R	V	T		R	I	N	I	N	O		E	N	M	
A	E	R	R	G	I	N	A	Y	I	O		E	A	A
B	M		E	I	N	A	F	C	F	D	P	R	C	C
L	A			I	C	I	G	U	T	I	A	S	E	I
E	K			S	K	L	E	L	M	R	F		O	
L	I	K	E	N	E	S	S	Z	A	L	E	O		U
D	N	O	P	S	E	R	O	T	Z	B	Y	N	L	S
	G						L	E	U	L		T	G	
G	N	I	N	O	S	A	E	R	G	R	N	E		

Puzzle # 30
ASSORTED WORDS 30

D			D	S	T	S	I	C	I	R	Y	L	M
E	I	E	C		E		P	E	R	S	O	N	S	E
A	T	S	D	O		R			L			R		R
L	N	A	I	E	M		U			A		E		R
	O	T	M	N	C	P		T			C	F		Y
	W	I	P	F	C	A	U	L	D	R	O	N	M
		N	S	L	E	A	T		U		R	L	A
		E	E	E	C		I		C	M	E	K
			S	P	H	T		B		S	X	E
			D	U	S	T	E	D		L		P	R
D	U	P	L	I	C	A	T	I	O	N		Y	L
S	R	E	K	A	E	R	B	E	C	I			A
C	H	U	R	C	H	G	O	E	R	S			I
S	U	O	I	G	I	L	E	R	R	I			N
	Y	L	L	A	T	N	E	D	I	C	C	A	S

Puzzle # 31
ASSORTED WORDS 31

Puzzle # 32
ASSORTED WORDS 32

```
      G Y L L A N O I T A N
        N F R E T I C E N C E
        S I E P   H G
S A I U Q O L L O C I H
R E K C I H T T I T   A T
    S N U C K N S C E   M L
D T   O   L       A U I E   I Y
  E N   P   L       C H T R   N
S E T E   X B I R D E D I T
E   S A I   E   T         E
T     A G T D R E S S I N G S
T       E O A   E   I T
E       N R P   V   D R
E         U E M   O       A
S N A T C H E S D I       P
```

```
S N O I T A C I F I D O M
T A   M I D W I F E S
E S D E Z I R U T A I N I M
R S L S   T F U N K Y
T R U E A R   S Y R
A O R   D T E   E E Y         P
R R E T I O I T C I V T       L
N S D O S S B P H O T R A     U
I   L I C K E A A G U S U S M
S P Y L O Y S   P C I P U S B
H O   E M L T   E     F I D I
I T   T P I O   L         N N
N T   T O G W G U A R D I N G
G E   E S H N E O L O G I S M
  R   D E T A R E C R A C N I
```

```
    R E I L E P A H S   T R
    T N A S S I O R C   H U
S T N E M P R A C S E   R N
      A R T I E S T     O D
  I N T E R R O G A T I O N O
      B U I L D U P S   G W
D O E R S S E N R E G A E I N
      H E R N I A       N S
T N A R I P S A         G W
N A M W O H S   I N D O O R A
G A Y E S T D E V O R P E R D
      G N I T S I E H       I
      F A C E L I F T S E
      T S E I F F U R C S
    C R O S S I N G
```

```
    S S E N I T L I U G     U
Y R A C I V A Q E Z I L Y T S
S T N A I G   P U           H
P   S R E G N A D A         E
E N E R G I Z E D A I     I R
R   D B I         E N   M
I   O   H           D T P M
S   W M S T N E I L A S R O
H   D L   I   D E P L O R E D
I   E     C   O       S E
N   R N     I   O     S R
G   S   N     L   L   I N
S E C I R F I T N E D B   N I
S E I D R A T B E H I N D G T
    K C A B S A V N A C Y
```

Puzzle # 37
ASSORTED WORDS 37

			R	E	F	E	R	E	N	D	U	M	S
			Y	C	N	A	N	G	I	L	A	M	
W	I	R	R	I	G	A	T	E	D	H			
C	A	E			S	P	A	W	N	S			
E	O	I	Y	T	I	M	E	R	T	X	E	A	
S	L	N	L		A			I			I	N	
H		T	F	S		G			B			R	G
R	B	A	T	I	N	G	E			B			F
I	R		N	A	R	E	I	L	D	D	U	C	
V	E		T	R	M			E			H		
E		K		I		E			D				
L			C		C		D						
L	D	O	R	K	I	E	S	T					
E					S	P	L	E	N	A	R	Y	
D			L	I	Q	U	I	D	A	T	O	R	

Puzzle # 38
ASSORTED WORDS 38

H	E	E	D	L	E	S	S	N	E	S	S	I		I
	Y	S	D	R	S					M		N		
A		Y	R	T	E	E	U			P	R	S		
	L	R	L	T	A	H	D	O		R	O	E		
U		L	E	L	E	R	S	N	R		E	U	M	
P		I	F	A	G	R	A	E	A		S	N	I	
S	H	F		D	U	C	D	I	W	M	C	S	D	N
T	E		I		E	L	I	A	E	N	R	I	H	
A	M	S		R		C	G	R	G	R	U	O	O	T
G	L		N		E	Y		E	Y		I	N	U	I
E	I			E		S	K		N	L	S	I	S	N
D	N		D	U	P	L	I	C	A	T	E	S	E	G
	E				X		D	O		R	T	S		
Y	R	O	I	R	P		E		E	T	S		U	
	C	I	B	M	A	I				S	S			C

Puzzle # 39
ASSORTED WORDS 39

	G	A	M	B	O	L	L	I	N	G				N
F	I	N	A	N	C	E	D						L	E
	T		I	R	R	E	F	U	T	A	B	L	E	R
	S	S		T		G				D		T	N	V
B	T	T	I		C		N			I		A	G	O
T	E	S	S	S	S	I		I		S		S	T	U
D	S	T	E	E	N	N	D		R	T		T	H	S
	E	E	T	B	R	O	A	D	S	E		E	I	N
	G	D	S	O	R	E	C	P	A	N	K	R	L	E
		N	U	U	R	E	T		H	D		C	Y	S
			I	R	T	S	P	N		S			I	S
			P	T	B		U	I		I				B
S	P	O	U	T	A	N	O		S	S		D		
			H	T	E	I	T	H	G	I	E			
	N	E	R	V	E	S	L				D			

Puzzle # 40
ASSORTED WORDS 40

D	T			S	N	D	O	L	M	E	N		H	
	E	S			E	E	E	S				U	I	
	S	R	I			I	H	P	E			N	N	
S	S	R	E	N	R	S	D	C	P	C		K	C	
D	N	M	E	T	R	E	S	O	T	O	A	E	U	
S	E	O	S	U	R	E	O	E	B	I	H	T	R	R
M	L	L	O	I	Q	A	T	G	L	Y	K	C	I	I
O	E	A	B	B	C	C	B	N	H	E	S	N	O	
N		R	G	B	A	R	A		I	C	V	U	G	U
K	T		E	E	I	B	O	L		R	O	B	S	
E	I		S	R	N		X			U	L			
Y	N			C	O	R	S	E	T	E	D	H		
E	G		T	N	E	I	C	I	F	F	E	O	C	
D	E		F	O	R	E	S	T	E	R				
	S		C	I	M	R	E	D	O	P	Y	H		

122

Puzzle # 41
ASSORTED WORDS 41

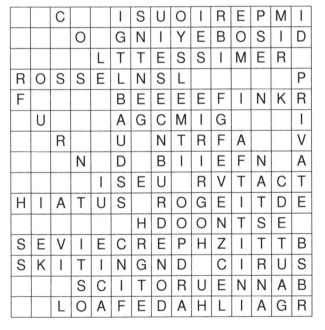

	S	E	Z	I	S	A	H	P	M	E			L
		G			E	F	E	T	I	S	H	I	
	D		A			L	A			E		A	
	D	O			R			B	I		R		B
		N	W			N			B	R	V		I
	G		E	S			E			I	E		L
M	C	O	N	S	C	I	O	U	S	L	Y	R	S	I
U	E		I	E	S	N		D			S	D	T
S	D	L		Y	L	R	A	G	G	E	B			I
I	E				E	V	N	N		O			E
C	V	C			S	I	E	I		O			S
I	E		E	C	Y	N	I	C	T	P		C
A	N			I			H	E	I	R
N	S	L	A	I	V	I	R	T	C	S	H	A
S	K	N	O	B	B	I	E	S	T			W	H

Puzzle # 42
ASSORTED WORDS 42

	S	A	R	D	Y	H	H	O	G	W	A	S	H
	C		G	C	E	M	D		S
S	O	Y		A	D	T	U	I	D	P
	N		T	L	R	E	C	E	T	E	M
	V	I		I	E	D	I	E	C	C	T	I
	O		A	S	N	P	E	F	L	Y	H	P	P
	O	Y		P	T	B	E	A	N	I	P	L	E	O
H	F	S		R	H	N	L	M	H	I	M	M		D
A	F		I	E	C	O	O	A	C	N	M	O
R	I		C	N	H		C	O			G	U	C
M	C		E	I	A			D				M
O	E		S	C	N	O	C	A	R	I	N	A
N	S	H	T	E	I	T	H	G	I	E		E
I		C	A	R	E	L	E	S	S	N	E	S	S
C	O	U	N	T	E	R	P	A	N	E

Puzzle # 43
ASSORTED WORDS 43

	C			I	S	U	O	I	R	E	P	M	I
		O		G	N	I	Y	E	B	O	S	I	D
			L	T	T	E	S	S	I	M	E	R
R	O	S	S	E	L	N	S	L					P
F				B	E	E	E	E	F	I	N	K	R
	U			A	G	C	M	I	G				I
		R		U		N	T	R	F	A			V
			N		D		B	I	I	E	F	N		A
				I	S	E	U		R	V	T	A	C	T
H	I	A	T	U	S		R	O	G	E	I	T	D	E
					H	D	O	O	N	T	S	E
S	E	V	I	E	C	R	E	P	H	Z	I	T	T	B
S	K	I	T	I	N	G	N	D		C	I	R	U	S
			S	C	I	T	O	R	U	E	N	N	A	B
		L	O	A	F	E	D	A	H	L	I	A	G	R

Puzzle # 44
ASSORTED WORDS 44

E	T	A	I	R	U	X	U	L
	L	A	I	N	N	E	L	L	I	M
M	S	I	N	O	I	S	S	E	R	P	M	I
	E	M	A	N	C	I	P	A	T	E	S
P		G	O	G	A	M	E	D	E	P	O	D
H	R	D	G	R	E	N		C	R	A	C	K	E	R
A	O	A	E	N	E	Z	I	S	R	T
L	M	M	V	F	I	S	A	T	E	A	I
F	E	N		I	A	R	P	E	O	R	L	F		G
P	N	A		P	M	E	I	L	O	O	L	Y	R
E	A	B			E	A	G	R	S	H	N	I	A
N	D	L			R	T	N	A	P	S	S	P
N	E	E		Y	L	L	A	N	O	I	T	O	M	E
Y	G	N	I	N	R	A	E	L	E	R	F	O	R	S
	G	Y	N	E	C	O	L	O	G	Y		R	P

Puzzle # 45
ASSORTED WORDS 45

			S	E	I	K	O	O	R				R	
S	T	E	E	P	L	E	J	A	C	K			H	
	D			D	E	A	D	L	I	E	R		A	
	C	E	H	G	M	O	N	I	T	O	R	S		P
P	M	O	B	E	N		S	I	T	U	A	T	E	S
L	O	L	R	A	I		G							O
U	M	O	L	I	D	W	T		I					D
M	A		C	O	E	S	O	S		R			I	
E		D	U	H	I	F	T	R	E	V	O	C	Z	
S		D	C	R	E	E	D	S	O	C	G		B	E
		E	S		R			N		I		A		
D	I	S	C	O	M	M	O	D	E		E		D	
		T		R		D	E	S	U	R	E	D	N	U
			S	E	U	G	O	G	A	D	E	P		
	N	U	M	S	K	U	L	L	S					

Puzzle # 46
ASSORTED WORDS 46

M	I	S	C	A	R	R	I	A	G	E	S		
A	S	N	O	I	T	I	N	U	M				
	P		F	I	L	T	R	A	T	I	N	G	O
		T	S	E	I	C	N	A	F			I	X
D		T	N	A	H	C	R	E	M			N	Y
	E		C	E			T	E	L	T	N	U	A	G
D	D	K	O	O	S	A	E	C	I	U	L	S	D	E
M	E	E	R		M	S	L					V	N
R	O	L	T	O	D	M		L				I	A
O		I	I	R	W	L	A		O			S	T
M			S	M	O	R	E	N		C		A	I
P		O	T	I	S	E	I	D		A		B	N
E		N		E	T		V	F	E		T	L	G
R		E			N	E		O	N	R		E
S	S	N	W	O	D	B	U	R			I	S

Puzzle # 47
ASSORTED WORDS 47

	N	I	R	E	C	Y	L	G	O	R	T	I	N
		F			P	I	S	T	A	C	H	I	O	S
		N	O	I	T	A	L	E	R	R	O	C
N	O	I	T	A	R	O	P	R	O	C
C		L	S	N	O	I	T	A	C	I	R	B	A	F
R		E	D	E	N	E	V	A	R	T	N	O	C
A		D	R	E	H	P	A	R	G	O	M	E	D
F	L	A	I	C	O	S	A	D	N	E	B	N	U
T			H	S	I	K	C	A	L	B
I		D	E	Y	A	R	G	N	I	R	I	A	H	C
N		D		L	L	Y	H	P	O	R	O	L	H	C
E	S	E	R	O	F	A	N	I	P	M
S			O	U	T	E	R	S			D
S	E	T	A	C	I	T	N	E	H	T	U	A
		F	O	N	D	N	E	S	S

Puzzle # 48
ASSORTED WORDS 48

	R	C		T	A	W	D	R	I	N	E	S	S
F		E	Y	R	N	O	C	L	A	F
L	H	R	E	L		G					S
O	O	I		N	D	G	N	I	R	R	A	M	T
C	B	S			A	E	D	I	B	L	E	I	E	L
K	O	E			D	C	T		P			R	M	I
S	E	M	U	S	N	O	C	A		A		K	B	B
	D		G				I	U	L		R		L	E
W	I	G	E	O	N	S		L	B	E		G	O	R
H	A	R	P	O	O	N	E	D	I		B		R	A
	S	E	R	U	C	S	B	O		E			T
				F	E	N	C	E	S				I
S	D	I	A	M	D	N	A	H					O
	P	E	R	S	U	A	S	I	V	E			N
			R	E	S	T	R	I	C	T	I	V	E	S

124

Puzzle # 49
ASSORTED WORDS 49

```
C . . E B D E H T U O M . . .
. I . . A C O U N T E S S . .
. . D S . R R . . . . H . . .
. . . E F R N A W O R K O U T
A S S U R E S A C S . . V . R
. . . . T I M H H Q . E . U .
L . . R T . L U K E U D . A .
. U . . E S . E I A . I . N .
A C C E P T I N G B N R . R T
. S N A K E S G O S . A T . E
. S E I R U C . G O T . R S D
. . . A . . . O L R . E . A .
. . S T C I V E M L A . . G .
. T S E I C E E L F . S A P .
C O M P U T E R I Z E S . B S
```

Puzzle # 50
ASSORTED WORDS 50

```
. . R S . M A N I F E S T S .
. . A . R Y T I N I V I D . .
. . D . E T N A L P M I . P .
N I I . G S . . . D D S . O .
O N A . L . A . R E S . . U .
N N . O . D E . A S I . . L .
R V C T . C E E . T I P M . T
I E E . S K . V . N A U . I .
G R O S S E D E E . E I L . C
I I S . N S L . E D R A . E .
D F . T . S H O R E R I T R D
. I . . Y P . P L . . N I . B
. E Y L D I V I L C . G N . .
. S . . E N N . . . L G . . .
S E S E Y L . G . . . . Y . .
```

Puzzle # 51
ASSORTED WORDS 51

```
. . . D E R E P A I D . . . P
M S L I V E D E R A D . . . L
A . S . D . . . T . . . P E .
R . . E C E T A L O I V N I A
A . S . N U M N . . O . . T S
T . P Y B L D E I . . B . C A
H S O S L A U D H A . . . H N
O E I . N L L F L C P . . F T
N T L T . U U K H I S E . O E
E E E D A . G F I T E . R R R
R A R . R M . G T E I S . K .
S C . . U A . L H S A T . . .
. H . . . C R . I G T F . . .
S N I K S G I P D . N I . . .
. . . . F I Z Z I N G R . . .
```

Puzzle # 52
ASSORTED WORDS 52

```
D S . . . . . P . . . . . . .
. E E Y G O L O C A M R A H P
. . M T S M I A L C C A . . .
P I . R O S E N I T N E L A V
E M S L A N I G I R O B A C .
R M . . H W K R O W G E L . .
S O . . . O G N I L L E U R G
U R . G N I N I A R T S E R .
A T . T E U Q I R B . N . . .
S A . G N I T T E N . . E . .
I L . . . Y L M O D N A R P .
O I N N I J G N I D U O R H S
N Z . . P E R S P E C T I V E
S E E Z I R A T I L I M E D .
. D E I F I T N E D I S I M .
```

125

SUDOKU SOLUTIONS

Puzzle #1

4	3	5	8	2	6	7	1	9
7	1	6	3	4	9	5	8	2
9	2	8	5	1	7	3	4	6
1	8	4	6	9	3	2	7	5
6	7	2	4	8	5	1	9	3
5	9	3	2	7	1	4	6	8
3	4	9	7	5	8	6	2	1
8	5	7	1	6	2	9	3	4
2	6	1	9	3	4	8	5	7

Puzzle #2

2	7	4	5	3	1	8	6	9
6	9	3	4	8	2	1	5	7
5	1	8	9	7	6	4	2	3
9	8	6	7	2	4	3	1	5
1	4	5	3	6	9	7	8	2
7	3	2	1	5	8	9	4	6
3	2	1	6	4	7	5	9	8
8	5	9	2	1	3	6	7	4
4	6	7	8	9	5	2	3	1

Puzzle #3

4	7	9	6	3	2	5	8	1
2	3	8	1	4	5	7	6	9
6	1	5	7	9	8	4	2	3
1	6	3	5	8	7	9	4	2
5	8	4	3	2	9	6	1	7
7	9	2	4	1	6	3	5	8
9	2	6	8	7	4	1	3	5
3	5	7	2	6	1	8	9	4
8	4	1	9	5	3	2	7	6

Puzzle #4

5	2	1	6	9	3	7	8	4
9	8	6	4	7	1	3	5	2
3	7	4	8	5	2	1	6	9
7	5	3	2	6	9	8	4	1
4	1	2	7	3	8	5	9	6
8	6	9	1	4	5	2	3	7
1	4	5	9	8	7	6	2	3
6	3	7	5	2	4	9	1	8
2	9	8	3	1	6	4	7	5

Puzzle #5

1	7	8	3	6	2	5	9	4
9	3	4	7	1	5	6	8	2
2	5	6	8	9	4	1	7	3
8	2	3	5	4	1	9	6	7
5	9	1	6	2	7	4	3	8
4	6	7	9	3	8	2	1	5
3	8	2	1	5	6	7	4	9
6	4	9	2	7	3	8	5	1
7	1	5	4	8	9	3	2	6

Puzzle #6

1	2	4	3	7	9	6	5	8
9	3	6	5	4	8	1	2	7
8	7	5	6	2	1	9	4	3
6	9	1	2	8	3	4	7	5
5	4	2	1	6	7	3	8	9
3	8	7	4	9	5	2	1	6
4	5	8	9	3	2	7	6	1
7	6	9	8	1	4	5	3	2
2	1	3	7	5	6	8	9	4

Puzzle #7

7	8	2	5	6	1	9	4	3
3	9	4	2	7	8	1	6	5
6	1	5	9	3	4	7	8	2
2	7	3	1	8	5	4	9	6
5	4	8	6	9	3	2	7	1
9	6	1	4	2	7	5	3	8
8	5	9	3	4	2	6	1	7
1	3	6	7	5	9	8	2	4
4	2	7	8	1	6	3	5	9

Puzzle #8

7	8	5	6	4	2	9	3	1
9	6	1	5	8	3	2	4	7
2	3	4	7	9	1	8	6	5
6	1	8	2	5	9	3	7	4
3	4	7	8	1	6	5	9	2
5	9	2	4	3	7	6	1	8
1	5	9	3	7	8	4	2	6
4	2	3	1	6	5	7	8	9
8	7	6	9	2	4	1	5	3

Puzzle #9

5	6	8	3	9	1	7	4	2
9	1	2	4	7	6	3	8	5
3	7	4	8	5	2	9	6	1
6	3	5	1	4	9	8	2	7
2	8	1	5	6	7	4	9	3
4	9	7	2	8	3	5	1	6
1	5	3	9	2	4	6	7	8
7	2	9	6	3	8	1	5	4
8	4	6	7	1	5	2	3	9

Puzzle #10

9	2	7	5	3	8	6	4	1
5	8	4	6	2	1	9	7	3
6	1	3	4	7	9	2	5	8
7	9	1	2	4	5	3	8	6
2	3	5	8	9	6	7	1	4
8	4	6	7	1	3	5	2	9
4	5	9	3	8	2	1	6	7
3	7	2	1	6	4	8	9	5
1	6	8	9	5	7	4	3	2

Puzzle #11

6	7	5	3	1	9	8	2	4
8	1	3	4	5	2	7	9	6
9	4	2	7	6	8	3	1	5
3	6	1	8	2	5	4	7	9
4	2	8	9	3	7	5	6	1
7	5	9	6	4	1	2	8	3
5	8	6	1	7	4	9	3	2
2	3	7	5	9	6	1	4	8
1	9	4	2	8	3	6	5	7

Puzzle #12

9	1	5	8	3	7	4	2	6
6	4	7	9	5	2	1	3	8
8	3	2	1	4	6	5	7	9
7	5	8	3	6	4	9	1	2
1	2	4	5	9	8	3	6	7
3	6	9	7	2	1	8	4	5
4	7	1	6	8	9	2	5	3
5	9	6	2	1	3	7	8	4
2	8	3	4	7	5	6	9	1

Puzzle #13

2	6	4	1	8	9	5	3	7
3	8	7	5	6	4	1	9	2
5	9	1	2	7	3	8	4	6
8	2	9	6	1	7	3	5	4
7	1	6	3	4	5	9	2	8
4	5	3	9	2	8	6	7	1
6	3	8	4	5	2	7	1	9
9	7	2	8	3	1	4	6	5
1	4	5	7	9	6	2	8	3

Puzzle #14

3	2	7	5	8	1	9	4	6
4	5	1	6	9	3	2	7	8
8	6	9	7	2	4	5	3	1
5	3	4	9	6	2	8	1	7
2	1	8	3	4	7	6	5	9
7	9	6	1	5	8	4	2	3
9	7	2	4	1	6	3	8	5
1	4	5	8	3	9	7	6	2
6	8	3	2	7	5	1	9	4

Puzzle #15

3	9	8	1	5	4	6	2	7
1	5	7	2	6	3	4	8	9
6	2	4	7	8	9	5	1	3
4	6	3	8	1	7	2	9	5
8	7	9	5	4	2	1	3	6
5	1	2	3	9	6	8	7	4
9	8	6	4	3	1	7	5	2
2	3	1	6	7	5	9	4	8
7	4	5	9	2	8	3	6	1

Puzzle #16

3	4	1	9	7	8	6	2	5
7	8	2	3	6	5	1	4	9
6	9	5	4	1	2	7	3	8
9	5	7	8	2	1	4	6	3
8	3	4	7	9	6	5	1	2
1	2	6	5	3	4	9	8	7
5	1	3	6	8	9	2	7	4
4	6	8	2	5	7	3	9	1
2	7	9	1	4	3	8	5	6

Puzzle #17

1	8	6	9	7	5	4	2	3
3	4	2	6	1	8	5	9	7
5	9	7	3	4	2	1	6	8
4	1	3	5	2	6	8	7	9
7	6	5	8	9	4	3	1	2
9	2	8	7	3	1	6	4	5
2	5	9	4	6	3	7	8	1
6	3	1	2	8	7	9	5	4
8	7	4	1	5	9	2	3	6

Puzzle #18

7	1	6	5	3	4	9	8	2
9	2	8	6	7	1	5	4	3
4	5	3	8	2	9	7	6	1
1	4	5	2	9	3	6	7	8
6	3	7	1	4	8	2	9	5
2	8	9	7	5	6	1	3	4
3	6	2	4	1	7	8	5	9
8	9	1	3	6	5	4	2	7
5	7	4	9	8	2	3	1	6

Puzzle #19

4	5	1	8	9	7	6	3	2
2	3	6	4	5	1	8	7	9
8	7	9	3	6	2	4	5	1
9	8	4	5	7	3	1	2	6
3	6	7	2	1	8	5	9	4
1	2	5	6	4	9	3	8	7
5	9	2	1	3	6	7	4	8
6	4	8	7	2	5	9	1	3
7	1	3	9	8	4	2	6	5

Puzzle #20

2	5	6	4	3	8	9	1	7
8	9	7	5	2	1	3	6	4
1	4	3	9	6	7	8	5	2
3	6	9	2	8	5	4	7	1
4	8	2	1	7	6	5	3	9
7	1	5	3	9	4	6	2	8
6	2	8	7	5	9	1	4	3
5	3	4	8	1	2	7	9	6
9	7	1	6	4	3	2	8	5

Puzzle #21

6	8	5	7	4	1	2	3	9
7	1	4	2	3	9	6	5	8
2	3	9	5	8	6	1	7	4
5	6	1	8	9	4	7	2	3
3	4	2	6	7	5	8	9	1
8	9	7	3	1	2	4	6	5
1	7	3	9	6	8	5	4	2
4	5	6	1	2	3	9	8	7
9	2	8	4	5	7	3	1	6

Puzzle #22

6	5	8	2	7	1	9	4	3
1	4	3	8	6	9	2	5	7
9	2	7	3	5	4	8	6	1
5	9	4	7	8	2	1	3	6
8	3	1	4	9	6	7	2	5
2	7	6	1	3	5	4	9	8
7	8	9	6	2	3	5	1	4
3	1	5	9	4	7	6	8	2
4	6	2	5	1	8	3	7	9

Puzzle #23

8	5	4	9	3	7	2	6	1
7	9	6	8	2	1	4	5	3
1	3	2	4	6	5	8	7	9
6	2	1	7	4	9	5	3	8
5	7	3	6	1	8	9	2	4
4	8	9	3	5	2	7	1	6
9	6	7	2	8	3	1	4	5
3	1	8	5	7	4	6	9	2
2	4	5	1	9	6	3	8	7

Puzzle #24

4	9	6	5	1	2	8	3	7
7	8	3	4	6	9	5	1	2
2	5	1	7	3	8	4	6	9
3	2	9	6	4	7	1	5	8
8	1	4	9	2	5	6	7	3
5	6	7	1	8	3	9	2	4
6	3	5	8	7	4	2	9	1
1	7	8	2	9	6	3	4	5
9	4	2	3	5	1	7	8	6

Puzzle #25

7	3	6	1	5	2	8	4	9
8	9	4	3	6	7	2	1	5
1	5	2	9	8	4	7	3	6
9	7	8	5	3	6	1	2	4
6	2	1	4	7	9	5	8	3
3	4	5	2	1	8	9	6	7
4	1	3	8	9	5	6	7	2
5	8	7	6	2	3	4	9	1
2	6	9	7	4	1	3	5	8

Puzzle #26

9	4	8	6	2	7	5	1	3
1	3	7	4	5	8	9	2	6
6	2	5	9	1	3	8	4	7
8	7	2	3	9	6	4	5	1
4	9	1	5	7	2	3	6	8
3	5	6	1	8	4	7	9	2
2	8	9	7	4	1	6	3	5
7	6	4	2	3	5	1	8	9
5	1	3	8	6	9	2	7	4

Puzzle #27

8	9	2	6	3	5	7	1	4
1	4	5	7	9	8	6	3	2
3	7	6	2	1	4	8	5	9
4	5	8	1	2	3	9	6	7
2	3	7	9	5	6	4	8	1
6	1	9	4	8	7	3	2	5
5	2	4	3	6	9	1	7	8
9	6	1	8	7	2	5	4	3
7	8	3	5	4	1	2	9	6

Puzzle #28

4	3	8	1	5	6	2	7	9
9	6	5	3	7	2	1	8	4
1	7	2	8	4	9	3	5	6
3	4	9	7	8	1	5	6	2
8	2	1	6	3	5	9	4	7
7	5	6	2	9	4	8	1	3
5	1	3	9	6	7	4	2	8
6	8	4	5	2	3	7	9	1
2	9	7	4	1	8	6	3	5

Puzzle #29

4	1	2	5	9	3	8	6	7
7	8	9	1	6	4	2	5	3
3	5	6	7	8	2	9	4	1
6	3	1	9	2	7	5	8	4
9	2	5	8	4	1	7	3	6
8	7	4	3	5	6	1	9	2
1	4	8	2	3	9	6	7	5
5	6	7	4	1	8	3	2	9
2	9	3	6	7	5	4	1	8

Puzzle #30

7	2	6	3	9	8	5	4	1
1	5	9	7	6	4	3	8	2
8	3	4	5	1	2	9	7	6
5	4	2	8	3	9	6	1	7
6	7	8	1	2	5	4	3	9
3	9	1	6	4	7	2	5	8
9	6	7	4	8	3	1	2	5
2	8	3	9	5	1	7	6	4
4	1	5	2	7	6	8	9	3

Puzzle #31

4	8	3	1	7	9	5	6	2
9	2	1	4	5	6	8	3	7
5	7	6	8	2	3	1	9	4
6	4	5	2	9	1	7	8	3
2	1	7	3	4	8	6	5	9
8	3	9	7	6	5	4	2	1
7	5	8	9	1	2	3	4	6
1	6	2	5	3	4	9	7	8
3	9	4	6	8	7	2	1	5

Puzzle #32

8	9	4	2	7	6	1	5	3
2	3	1	4	8	5	9	6	7
5	7	6	1	9	3	4	2	8
1	4	9	3	6	7	5	8	2
6	2	5	9	4	8	7	3	1
7	8	3	5	1	2	6	9	4
3	1	7	6	2	9	8	4	5
4	6	2	8	5	1	3	7	9
9	5	8	7	3	4	2	1	6

Puzzle #33

8	6	4	9	2	3	7	5	1
9	5	7	4	6	1	3	2	8
1	2	3	8	7	5	9	4	6
2	1	8	7	3	6	4	9	5
4	3	9	5	1	8	6	7	2
5	7	6	2	9	4	8	1	3
6	9	5	3	4	2	1	8	7
3	4	2	1	8	7	5	6	9
7	8	1	6	5	9	2	3	4

Puzzle #34

8	2	9	7	6	5	4	1	3
5	3	4	9	2	1	8	6	7
6	7	1	8	3	4	9	2	5
3	5	7	6	9	2	1	4	8
4	8	2	1	5	7	6	3	9
1	9	6	3	4	8	7	5	2
9	6	8	2	1	3	5	7	4
2	1	5	4	7	9	3	8	6
7	4	3	5	8	6	2	9	1

Puzzle #35

8	2	6	1	9	4	3	5	7
3	4	5	7	6	8	1	9	2
7	1	9	5	2	3	6	4	8
1	9	8	2	7	5	4	6	3
4	3	7	6	8	1	5	2	9
6	5	2	4	3	9	8	7	1
5	7	3	9	1	6	2	8	4
9	8	4	3	5	2	7	1	6
2	6	1	8	4	7	9	3	5

Puzzle #36

7	5	2	8	4	6	1	9	3
9	4	1	2	7	3	5	6	8
8	6	3	1	5	9	2	4	7
1	9	5	7	6	8	3	2	4
2	8	6	9	3	4	7	5	1
4	3	7	5	1	2	9	8	6
5	2	4	3	8	7	6	1	9
3	1	8	6	9	5	4	7	2
6	7	9	4	2	1	8	3	5

Puzzle #37

6	2	7	8	9	5	3	4	1
3	5	8	1	2	4	9	6	7
4	9	1	3	6	7	5	8	2
8	3	9	5	4	2	7	1	6
5	7	6	9	8	1	4	2	3
2	1	4	7	3	6	8	5	9
7	8	2	4	1	3	6	9	5
9	6	5	2	7	8	1	3	4
1	4	3	6	5	9	2	7	8

Puzzle #38

8	3	5	4	2	7	6	9	1
6	1	7	5	9	8	3	4	2
9	2	4	1	6	3	5	8	7
2	5	8	3	7	4	1	6	9
4	7	6	9	1	2	8	5	3
1	9	3	8	5	6	2	7	4
3	4	2	7	8	5	9	1	6
5	6	9	2	4	1	7	3	8
7	8	1	6	3	9	4	2	5

Puzzle #39

2	4	1	9	3	5	6	8	7
3	7	8	6	1	2	9	4	5
9	6	5	7	4	8	1	3	2
1	8	2	3	5	9	4	7	6
5	9	4	2	7	6	8	1	3
7	3	6	4	8	1	2	5	9
8	5	9	1	6	7	3	2	4
4	2	7	8	9	3	5	6	1
6	1	3	5	2	4	7	9	8

Puzzle #40

8	1	3	6	7	2	4	9	5
7	9	2	5	4	3	1	8	6
6	4	5	9	8	1	7	2	3
2	8	6	4	9	5	3	1	7
4	3	1	2	6	7	8	5	9
9	5	7	1	3	8	6	4	2
1	6	8	7	5	9	2	3	4
5	2	4	3	1	6	9	7	8
3	7	9	8	2	4	5	6	1

Puzzle #41

4	1	6	2	7	5	3	8	9
3	7	2	8	6	9	1	5	4
8	5	9	3	1	4	6	7	2
9	8	1	6	2	3	7	4	5
7	6	3	4	5	8	9	2	1
5	2	4	7	9	1	8	6	3
2	4	8	9	3	6	5	1	7
6	3	5	1	4	7	2	9	8
1	9	7	5	8	2	4	3	6

Puzzle #42

7	2	9	5	8	3	6	1	4
8	4	3	6	9	1	7	2	5
1	5	6	7	2	4	8	3	9
2	6	7	9	5	8	3	4	1
3	8	5	4	1	2	9	7	6
9	1	4	3	6	7	2	5	8
4	3	1	8	7	9	5	6	2
5	9	2	1	3	6	4	8	7
6	7	8	2	4	5	1	9	3

Puzzle #43

1	7	6	3	4	2	5	9	8
3	8	5	9	1	6	7	4	2
2	4	9	5	7	8	3	6	1
5	9	2	4	6	1	8	3	7
4	1	7	8	2	3	6	5	9
8	6	3	7	5	9	1	2	4
6	3	1	2	9	7	4	8	5
9	5	8	1	3	4	2	7	6
7	2	4	6	8	5	9	1	3

Puzzle #44

9	5	1	2	8	6	3	4	7
3	7	8	1	5	4	2	9	6
6	2	4	7	3	9	8	5	1
7	4	9	3	2	1	6	8	5
1	8	6	4	9	5	7	3	2
2	3	5	8	6	7	4	1	9
8	1	7	5	4	2	9	6	3
4	6	2	9	1	3	5	7	8
5	9	3	6	7	8	1	2	4

Puzzle #45

5	3	1	2	6	9	4	8	7
7	6	8	1	3	4	5	2	9
2	4	9	5	7	8	1	3	6
4	2	6	3	5	1	7	9	8
9	5	3	7	8	2	6	1	4
1	8	7	9	4	6	3	5	2
8	7	2	4	1	3	9	6	5
6	1	5	8	9	7	2	4	3
3	9	4	6	2	5	8	7	1

Puzzle #46

7	2	5	4	6	8	1	3	9
1	8	6	5	9	3	2	7	4
9	4	3	1	7	2	5	8	6
4	1	2	7	3	6	9	5	8
3	9	7	8	1	5	4	6	2
6	5	8	9	2	4	3	1	7
5	7	4	3	8	9	6	2	1
2	3	1	6	4	7	8	9	5
8	6	9	2	5	1	7	4	3

Puzzle #47

5	6	2	1	3	8	7	9	4
4	1	3	6	9	7	2	8	5
9	8	7	2	4	5	3	6	1
3	2	9	4	6	1	8	5	7
6	4	8	5	7	3	9	1	2
1	7	5	8	2	9	6	4	3
7	5	6	9	1	2	4	3	8
2	9	1	3	8	4	5	7	6
8	3	4	7	5	6	1	2	9

Puzzle #48

9	1	5	6	2	8	3	4	7
2	3	8	4	5	7	6	9	1
7	4	6	9	3	1	5	2	8
8	5	2	7	6	9	1	3	4
1	6	3	2	8	4	7	5	9
4	9	7	3	1	5	2	8	6
5	8	4	1	7	2	9	6	3
3	2	1	8	9	6	4	7	5
6	7	9	5	4	3	8	1	2

Puzzle #49

5	2	8	1	6	9	4	7	3
6	9	7	3	2	4	8	5	1
4	3	1	5	7	8	9	6	2
7	6	9	8	3	2	1	4	5
2	4	5	6	9	1	3	8	7
1	8	3	7	4	5	6	2	9
9	1	2	4	8	7	5	3	6
8	5	6	2	1	3	7	9	4
3	7	4	9	5	6	2	1	8

Puzzle #50

3	7	4	8	6	5	9	1	2
5	9	8	1	4	2	6	7	3
1	2	6	9	3	7	5	4	8
8	4	1	7	5	9	2	3	6
6	5	2	4	1	3	7	8	9
7	3	9	6	2	8	1	5	4
2	1	5	3	9	4	8	6	7
9	8	3	5	7	6	4	2	1
4	6	7	2	8	1	3	9	5

Puzzle #51

7	4	3	8	1	6	5	2	9
8	5	6	2	9	7	3	4	1
2	1	9	3	4	5	7	6	8
9	7	5	4	3	1	6	8	2
3	8	4	7	6	2	1	9	5
6	2	1	5	8	9	4	7	3
5	6	8	1	2	4	9	3	7
4	3	7	9	5	8	2	1	6
1	9	2	6	7	3	8	5	4

Puzzle #52

6	5	2	3	4	7	1	8	9
1	7	9	2	6	8	4	3	5
3	8	4	1	5	9	7	2	6
9	4	6	8	1	3	2	5	7
7	1	8	5	2	6	3	9	4
5	2	3	9	7	4	6	1	8
8	6	5	7	3	1	9	4	2
4	9	1	6	8	2	5	7	3
2	3	7	4	9	5	8	6	1

Made in United States
North Haven, CT
15 June 2023

37760235R00076